Praise for

HERE by the OWL

"Gorgeous... I didn't want to stop reading."

-Heather Marshall, author of *The Thorn Tree*

"*Here By The Owl* is a heartstrung and emotionally transporting
love story. It's historically surprising in its specific details about
WWII, and also bound to its particular place and time in rural
Appalachia. The descriptions of setting and atmosphere are often
spectacular. There is so much to love here."

-Ashley Warlick, "award-winning author of *Seek the Living*

"A wonderful story... a thumping good yarn.
[Here by the Owl] has the makings of a film."

-Peter Kent, former host Clemson TV

This book is dedicated to

Janie Smith
"Granna"
Without whom, this book
would not exist

And

RG and Agnes Shipley
Without whom, this story
would not exist.

Published in the United States of America.

First edition.

Library of Congress Cataloguing in Publication Data:

Smith, Evan Peter, author.

Here by the Owl / Evan Peter Smith. –1st ed.

Greenville, S.C.: Claude Perry Press

Identifiers: ISBN: 9780578310787

Cover and Interior Design: Laura Allshouse

To Carol
— Congrats on your award
and thanks so much!

HERE

by the

OWL

EVAN PETER SMITH

— Evan

Claude Perry
PUBLISHING

AUTHOR'S NOTE

This book is a true story.

Any dialogue appearing within quotation marks has been taken verbatim from a letter, newspaper or magazine article, oral history interview, records from the National Archives, or firsthand accounts from the individuals who experienced for themselves the story that follows.

-Fvan Peter Smith, October 2021

I f you spend enough time in Watauga County, way out in the Blue Ridge Mountains of North Carolina, sooner or later you're bound to hear about the Shipleys.

He was 101 years old, and she was 96. Their marriage of 71 years all spent on a farm in the shadow of the mountains. *High Country Press,* one of the local mountain newspapers, called them "the first couple of agriculture in the High Country." There was something almost Biblical when it came to the two of them. Like the sugar maple trees that grow through the valley, the Shipleys seemed as if they'd always been here and always would be, their roots set deep in the loamy mountain soil.

But behind that old couple was a story most people in the mountains had never heard before, a story full of details too strange to believe. Crashed airplanes. A secret mission. A mysterious island where it rained constantly, yet the ground stayed bone dry. Nightmarish visions from a founding father of the US Air Force. And new life rising from a field of ashes.

The Shipleys always thought maybe one day they'd sit down and tell that story properly, but until then, their friends and neighbors in the Blue Ridge Mountains couldn't possibly know why they always held each other so close.

Why they never let go.

PART ONE
CITY GIRL

CHAPTER 1

⊷❦ ❧⊶

T he world was on fire when he saw her for the first time.
Newspaper headlines warned of merchant boats full
of civilians exploding across the Atlantic. Tank blitzes
traversed Northern Africa, scarring the desert. Bodies floated
in the bamboo-tangled swamps of Chinese villages after Japanese airstrikes. Russia was preparing for Nazi invasion. Day
and night, bombs kept falling in England and Germany, the
blasts flattening schools, museums and governmental buildings, demolishing homes and apartments, smoldering alley-
ways and sidewalks. The ungodly inferno spared not even the
oldest of churches, melting stained glass scenes of angels and
redemption into scorched nightmares right from the Book
of Revelation.

In Independence, Virginia, a small town near the border
with North Carolina – far away from any war, geographically
speaking – a young man by the name of Robert Gray Shipley
found himself in different kind of foreign territory. It was late
December 1940, an especially frigid night about a week or so
before Christmas. Warmly cocooned inside a small church, the
young Mr. Shipley glanced at the faces of the strangers around
him. He'd only recently arrived in Independence for his job
as a county extension agent. His work took him all over, visiting farmers and school agriculture programs, mopping up the
mess left behind from the Depression.

Tonight, his friend from work had brought him along to this
unfamiliar church for the late service. Wearing a black coat and

tie that fit just a little too tight over his broad shoulders, Robert Gray Shipley – RG, as most folks called him – fumbled a flimsy hymn book in his still-numb hands. Even inside, the smell of the cold clung to his jacket.

As the service began, the winter weather kept on bashing against the brick siding of the church, but at least inside the air was calm. Advent candles flickered gently by the altar. Holly and wreaths hung all around. The pastor's deep baritone reverberated down the aisle. RG was just glad to be inside where it was warm.

He couldn't say exactly when he noticed her, only that at some point or another during the service she simply appeared: a young woman up at the front, taking a seat behind the church piano. He watched her slide herself forward on the stool, then begin to play. Her hands flowed softly over the keys, the notes cascading like water droplets from tree branches after a rainstorm. She was such a tiny little thing, but soon the music rising from her fingertips soared into such a high volume that even the wind outside fell silent by comparison.

At the end of the service, as the rest of the congregation was shuffling out of the pews, the piano player was standing with a group of younger people who'd gathered at the front. The young woman looked even prettier up close: her brown hair glossy and curled, her large eyes gleaming mysteriously in the candlelight. She wore a fine dress that looked like something ready-made from a fancy department store, but for some reason, by the way it rippled as she turned to face him, by the way it fit her so perfectly, he knew right away she'd sewn the dress herself.

"Well, nice to meet you," she said when RG's friend from work introduced the two of them to each other.

He felt her gentle grip as they shook hands.

Talk among the group that night was all about the war. Just the day before, President Roosevelt had given a speech about shipping arms and supplies to England for the war effort, so speculation had been swirling over the question of whether the

United States was about to enter the fight. On the radio Roosevelt had said it was necessary for "the survival of democracy." Tonight, though, RG did his best to keep the conversation in lighter territory. He and the piano player exchanged pleasantries, asking where each other was from, how long they'd been in Independence, simple things. He found she was easy to talk to. Charming, funny. And it didn't hurt that she had a disarmingly beautiful smile. But just as they'd gotten started, it was already time to go. All the remaining congregants were now wrapping coats around themselves as they ventured forth outside into the cold.

He wrote down his mailing address for her. Unshy, she wrote down hers as well on a piece of scrap paper, telling RG to write her sometime, if he felt so inclined.

She signed the note: *Agnes*

Outside the church, he slid the paper in his jacket pocket and watched her disappear in the falling snow, Christmas lights blurring all around her.

No one could've expected RG to fall for a girl like Agnes, least of all him.

CHAPTER 2

M any years later, as an old man, RG had a saying he liked to tell his kids and grandkids about those early days of getting to know Agnes.

"I spent the first 30 years of my life looking for her," he'd tell them, "and if I'd spent another 30 years looking, or 60 years, or 90 years even, I still never would've found anyone like her."

No one could've expected RG to fall for a girl like her, least of all him. Agnes was from a different world. She was the daughter of a businessman who'd owned a general store in McGaheys-ville, Virginia, more than a week's ride by wagon from the valley in the mountains where RG was born.

Growing up, Agnes and her three younger sisters had sat prim and proper behind the counter of their father's store, watching as well-dressed townspeople flowed in through the doors. Her childhood had been Easter dresses and piano lessons, pretty hair bows and curtsies. Much later, when RG drove into town to meet her family for the first time, he would take note of the paved streets and stop signs, the smooth sidewalks, the modern electrical lampposts, and couldn't help but think, *She's a real city girl, huh?*

It was certainly a far cry from his childhood of roasting hogs and birthing cattle, but McGaheysville wasn't New York City either. The streetlights and stop signs had no bearing on the simple fact that everyone in town knew everyone else, and it remained a place where the rule of order was established not so much by the policeman's baton, but by hushed rumors in the church pews. If anything, the gossip traveled much quicker here than it did back in RG's hometown, because in the mountains of North Carolina you at least had to hop on a horse to tell your neighbor the latest.

By the time she graduated high school, Agnes' name was on the lips of those church gossipers more and more often. Unlike other young women who'd come of age in McGaheysville in the 1930s, she had never seemed too worried about keeping up appearances. Her neighbors on the block didn't have to do much more than peek through their curtains each morning to see Agnes stroll confidently out of her parents' front door, her head held high as she made her way down the street. They all knew she was heading to the bus station. Once there, Agnes would hop on the line and take her regular seat in the front.

RG may not have seen this part of her life, but he had an easy enough time picturing her: a young woman by herself, seated on the bus by the window, with her gloves and hand-made dress, the rumbling of the tires vibrating under her buckled shoes. To some of the other regular passengers, she would've looked curious sitting there. No husband or children with her. No parents or chaperone either. Alone, by all appearances, and what business did a young lady have traveling about by herself each day? What trouble was she up to? But Agnes paid them no mind. She was too busy gazing out the window at the passing land, as though browsing for something she might like to have for herself one day.

Chugging along, the bus would finally pull into the station at Harrisonburg, where Agnes would disembark, exit the station, and make her way down the road and up the hill, passing along the roadbed to the campus of Madison College. The wide college green was lush with gingko trees, American and Siberian elms, red oaks, black walnuts and Norway spruce. She strolled through the cool shade of their foliage along the path that led up to the Industrial School for Women. The elegant building stood like a courthouse at the end of the green, a stately and dignified compound of learning — and as it so happened, just about the only option around for a young woman desiring a college education.

Ever since she was a girl, Agnes had known in her bones that she would one day attend college. Her parents had agreed, having seen no reason why she or her sisters shouldn't expand their horizons beyond the quaint street signs and corner stores of McGaheysville. But the rest of the town had other notions. From an early age, all the girls in McGaheysville had it hammered into their pigtailed heads that respectable young women shouldn't be caught dead attending college. It was simply not the ladylike thing to do. There were a few who broke that rule, but just that: a few. And everyone knew who *those* girls were. They stood out like wine stains on a wedding gown — not that those girls would ever need wedding gowns, mind you. Everyone knew they lacked virtue, were less likely to find husbands, were in some way tarnished, or in the worst cases had deluded themselves into thinking they should strive for a career, the most lonesome of all fates.

Just about every other eligible girl in town had followed the rules. They'd gotten married, moved in with their husbands, had babies, and kept the home in order. So Agnes was quite a topic of curiosity amongst the gossiping crowd. Just a few summers prior, Agnes had taken first place in the regional beauty pageant. She would've had easy pickings for a husband, so why make things difficult for herself?

Or perhaps, they wondered, it was because of what had happened to her father's business? In which case, the gossipers agreed, all the more reason for her to find a husband with prospects.

Agnes knew there was only so much she could say in response to speculation like that. Beyond the polite smile and shoulder shrug, trying to convince them was like pushing water uphill with a rake. She didn't like the attention, for one, and besides, she'd rather spend her time on useful endeavors.

So, each morning as she walked into the college building in Harrisonburg, she'd make her way to the laboratory. There, she'd put on her white lab coat, her protective goggles and her sanitized gloves. The previous night's experiment would be waiting for further observation and markup. Looking through her microscope, Agnes would note the water content, the chemical makeup, what the seepage of fluids indicated. Always something new. Always a surprise, an unexpected development. That was what made it exciting. She was well aware of what folks said about her. She had ears, after all. And a part of her could understand what they meant. Some people just didn't understand why she spent all this time craning her neck and staring at such ordinary objects as a slice of an old Florida mango, or a petri dish of fermented syrup, or a rotting tomato. Why go through the trouble? But then, who says a moldy piece of fruit can't be just as fascinating as, say, the panorama of the night sky? Scientists had spent centuries gazing upward with telescopes at the mathematical beauty in the stars. What was so different about what she was doing? She just happened to be looking downward, using her microscope to see the beauty in the ordinary. But that close up, the architecture of a soggy mango was every bit as intricate and awe-inspiring as the constellations above.

To be fair, though, one did stink just a bit more.

Agnes studied home economics. To some, that meant baking cookies and twirling about in an apron, a silly excuse for real academic work. And Agnes found that to be so odd. For the life of her, she couldn't square how certain folks could condemn her educational aspirations as an arrogant overreach, while at the same time dismissing those pursuits as mere girlish dilly-dallying.

But so be it.

She preferred keeping her head down and going about her work, especially as it grew more complex the further along her

Agnes, seated in the middle of the bottom row, with her classmates and fellow home economics majors at Madison College.

studies advanced. By the time Agnes was a senior, she'd finally completed her thesis, her masterpiece. The work had a simple enough title, "Food Preparation," but the total tally of pages, on which she'd hand-written her research in small, looping cursive, on both sides of each sheet for that matter, including hand-drawn charts, graphs and data tables, came to number 212 sheets thick, with subtopics such as: *History of the Development of Scientific Canning; Tin Manufacturing; Bacteriology; Principles of Food Preservation; Commercial Ice-Making and Cold Storage;* and *Commercial Protein Use.*

The classroom was called a laboratory for good reason.

When she wasn't in the lab, Agnes took on odd jobs to help her family get by during the Depression. Her father had told her they'd be fine without any extra help, but she knew they were already in debt even before paying for her education. Especially now that her father's general store was gone, it felt only right to do what she could.

One of those jobs was repossessing vehicles for the owner of a car dealership in town. Agnes had a knack for the work, even if she didn't exactly enjoy confrontation – but that turned out to be her secret weapon. Folks who hadn't paid up what they owed for their cars might have been peering out their window, but they wouldn't think twice when Agnes strolled by: this cute girl with her light brown hair pinned back into innocent curls, her lipstick evenly applied, her posture straight and elegant like a lady. Just a minute or so later, however, after using the dealership key to slide gracefully into the driver's seat, Agnes would screech off in that car with both hands gripping the wheel tight. Her gift was to float under the radar, until the moment came to strike. Sometimes the delinquent car owner would even run after her down the road, shaking a fist in the air. People who happened to be out for an afternoon stroll would hear the roar of the engine as Agnes whipped around the corner, driving like a bank robber on the run, and they would shake their heads at the madness of it all.

It was a strange time in her life. Her friends from high school were bouncing newborn babies on their laps, giving their husbands kisses on the cheek, and making sure supper was on the table. Agnes, meanwhile, was either speed-racing in semi-stolen cars or peering at rotten food items through a microscope in a lab, filling pages and pages of notebooks with her observations about the chaotic beauty of decay.

A strange time, but life was good.

The best moments always came at the end of each day, when the halls of the Industrial School were quiet, when Agnes was tired in all the best ways. She would switch off the lights in the lab, place her white coat in her locker, and collect her things, then take the hushed bus ride from college back into town, followed by that long solitary walk from the station to her house.

Windows glowed in the homes she passed along the street. And if any of the curtains at those windows happened to inch back, and if any prying eyes happened to stare out at her, Agnes was too busy looking ahead to notice.

RG would learn all of this later, through her letters, and it was from these stories that he realized, almost by accident, that he was falling in love with her.

CHAPTER 3

❧❧

Mast General Store was a cozy gathering spot in RG's hometown of Valle Crucis, North Carolina, just down the road from his farmland in the town of Vilas. As a boy, he used to ride his pony there on errands for his mother. Now, in the winter of 1941, he parked his old Pontiac out in front of the store and walked inside quickly, heaving the door shut behind him to keep the cold at bay.

The potbelly stove sighed heat over the wooden floorboards. Men with hats in their hands would be talking amongst themselves in the corner, and women perused the aisles with baskets in their hands, while small kids stood on tiptoes around the barrels full of candy. Mast General Store was RG's regular pitstop whenever he needed anything for the farm, the logbook of his purchases going all the way back to when he was just a boy, on those errands to pick up fertilizer or nails or other basic needs. Now he made the same pitstops on his weekly return to his farm as a grown man.

After collecting what he needed, he would navigate his Pontiac along the steep, narrow and winding road that led back to his farm in Vilas, but he always stopped by the post office first to see if another letter from Agnes had showed up. In those early months of getting to know her, those letters were as vital as any nails or fertilizer or other farming supplies, if not more so.

RG was almost 30 years old when he met Agnes, more than old enough to start thinking about settling down. But the trouble was, where to find the time? His job as an extension agent kept him busy out in Grayson County, Virginia, and beyond, going around helping farmers and offering educational services, rarely staying still for long. When he wasn't working, he spent a few days a week back here on his farm in the mountains of North Carolina, where he grew crops and raised cattle and other livestock. He was already pulled in so many different directions.

But he'd still decided to write to Agnes after meeting her in that church, and it helped that she didn't seem to have any expectations from him, although judging by how quickly she wrote back, she didn't seem to *not* welcome hearing from him either.

RG wrote that it'd been nice to meet her.

She wrote back saying she'd thought so too.

He wrote back and then she wrote back.

He wrote, she wrote.

And on and on it went over the coming weeks, the two getting to know one another through messy cursive scribbled on cheap stationary paper, their letters growing gradually longer as snow piled up outside RG's farmhouse window.

He learned about Agnes' childhood in McGaheysville and her college years studying home economics. She told him about how after she'd graduated, she'd moved hours away from McGaheysville to her current home, Independence, Virginia, a town with a fitting name for a young woman seeking to branch out on her own. But her start there hadn't exactly been luxurious. After graduating college, Agnes had managed to find a room in house owned by a family named Rudy, but when cold weather arrived, Mrs. Rudy had decided she no longer wanted to heat the side of the house in which Agnes was living. Agnes was kicked out into the cold, quite literally, and only found solace when a kind couple named Mr. and Mrs. Moore took pity upon her and offered her a place to sleep in their kitchen pantry.

But even that was better than nothing. Around that time, Agnes had gotten a job as a teacher for the National Youth Administration, that New Deal agency President Roosevelt had created to provide opportunities for those who came up in the Depression. She loved the job. All her friends back home were married, but even later on, once she was well into her 20s, Agnes saw no need to settle down. She loved working and living on her own out in Independence. She'd since moved on from living in that pantry and was now situated in a boarding house with a few roommates. She had her own space, too, her own little room, and could decorate it as she pleased, could close the door and exhale alone in her own little pocket of the world — it was hers, no one else's.

By day she taught rural girls how to survive in tough times. She would've loved teaching them Shakespeare or how to play Frederic Chopin on the piano, but these were strictly practical lessons. Nutrition, healthcare, finances. Teenage mothers who hardly understood how they'd gotten those babies in the first place would come to her asking what to do, what *this* meant, what *that* was, and Agnes would show them. It was astounding to her sometimes how little these girls knew of the world. "One time, a girl boiled an ear of corn for several hours!" Agnes told RG in one letter. There were more than a few nights when she stayed up late worrying, but when she was able to see once malnourished and sickly infants return to her rosy-cheeked and giggling, and relieved young mothers hugging her with tears in their eyes, well, what could beat that?

Reading these stories in Agnes' letters over the coming weeks, something curious happened to RG. He found that time was changing. The hours and minutes slowed down between her letters arriving. Whenever he was waiting to hear back from her, time felt bloated and sluggish. He found himself stopping by the post office to check his mailbox more frequently than was logical.

On occasion he had to stop himself from writing to her, because whenever a new story or fresh idea popped into his head, he felt the sudden urge to put pen to paper and tell her about it.

It didn't have be important. Sometimes it could be downright goofy: a lamb with a funny haircut he'd seen, or a cow that kept bashing at a farmer's rear end. He just felt like letting her know. He knew sending two letters back-to-back wouldn't look very good. Too eager. And yet, sometimes he just couldn't help it.

"It looks like my pen is very anxious to write," he began one letter that winter. "Could this letter be too soon? It would be nice to talk to you again but since you did not even count that last call as a proper letter I thought I had better not try that again. Last month my telephone bill was so high anyway I asked my landlord if I could get a reduction after $10.50. No such luck."

They tried talking on the phone as much as they could, but calls cost real money, and making sure both of them would be there to talk took some coordination.

"If I should be able to, I will call you Friday night at 7:30," he wrote to her at the start of the week. "Don't wait up for the call though if you are busy and do not let me interfere with your weekend plans."

Later, after they'd scheduled times to meet in person for a couple of dates, he got bolder.

"It was so good to see you again Saturday night," he wrote. "I still think you live much, much too far away."

RG hadn't been alone before meeting Agnes. He'd gotten to know other young women through church or social gatherings, but none of them would have warranted a farmer like him writing such detailed and exposed letters.

"It was such a beautiful moonlit drive Sunday night as I came down the Blue Ridge Parkway all by myself," he wrote after seeing Agnes one night in early 1941. He described the stars, the "clouds drifting in very peacefully over the valley — and the moon glowing so bright."

It wasn't poetry, exactly, but it was close enough for a man who spent his days out with cattle and muddy hogs.

Somehow, without either of them ever being fully aware of it, they'd become a real couple, planning whatever time they had to be together. RG would put on his best coat and tie, while Agnes would wear one of the new dresses she'd sewn. They'd go bowling, maybe see a movie or a concert show. With her help, RG was learning to appreciate orchestral music. That is, RG was pretending to appreciate orchestral music to impress her. Agnes loved taking him to the Cooperative Concert Association's presentations of violinists and pianists performing the work of musicians with fancy names like Schumann, Szymanowski, Glazounoff and Tchaikovsky. RG noticed Agnes always saved the bulletin of each concert. "Keepsakes," she called them, slipping them in her purse.

Afterwards, they took long walks down Main Street of Independence. It was late winter still. Snow swirled around the lampposts while they walked, their shadows elongating and shortening as they moved under the light. All down the street American flags had been hung from every brick storefront, flapping in the wind behind them.

Elsewhere, the bombs kept falling.

The staff of the *Watauga Democrat*, the local newspaper, would go on to document the war's toll for the people of the mountains.

CHAPTER 4

⊹⊹⊱🌿⊰⊹⊹

O n the front page of the *Watauga Democrat,* the mountain newspaper that showed up once a week in RG's
mailbox, the headlines about the war overseas never
took up much space.

"World War Veterans Are Asked to Register," read one headline at the very bottom of the Feb. 6, 1941, edition's front page,
the story itself nothing more than a paragraph urging ex-service
men to register at the Legion hut so they may be contacted "in
case of emergency."

Another story wedged near the bottom ran with the headline
"Young Wataugan Highly Pleased with Army Life" and told the
story of one Claude Woodro Bentley of Valle Crucis, who was
among the first quota from Watauga County drafted under the
Selective Service Act. "Young Bentley," the article explained,
"is highly pleased with army life and is now head cook with a
monthly salary of $54.00. He says military training is most ben-
eficial and plans to enter the army for a three-year period when
his present one-year enlistment is completed."

There were occasional ruminations in the mountains about
the possibility of severe conflict, such as when a public forum
of 120 civilians was held to discuss the topic: "Whether Democracy Can Survive the Present Crisis." The article noted, "Those
who believe it can were in the majority."

By the start of spring, on the weekend RG met Agnes' family for
the first time, the United States Army had grown to more than 1

million enlisted men. The edition of the *Watauga Democrat* that showed up in RG's mailbox that morning had called it a "rapid expansion" as a precautionary measure, while the fighting continued overseas. RG was too busy getting ready that morning to read much into it, and he set the paper aside as he walked out the door.

He and Agnes had only been dating a few months, but she'd said she wanted to show him around her hometown. Knowing she wasn't especially fond of McGaheysville — too many bitter memories, too much gossip — RG figured this was just her way of letting her family get a good look at him. Whether that meant she wanted to show him off, or put him to the test, he wasn't sure.

Driving into her hometown, RG watched as the rolling hills of hibernating winter kudzu and dense evergreens suddenly cleared out, as if shorn away by pioneers — which of course it all had been, long ago. Now McGaheysville, Virginia, was an earnestly plucky town of storefronts and stop signs, resting in the shadow of Massanutten Mountain. At night in town, Agnes said, you could hear the howls of coyotes in the distance, the scraping and branch breaking of black bears, and the venomous Tambourine music of the rattlesnakes.

RG was less worried about rattlesnakes, and more worried about meeting Agnes' folks.

But he shouldn't have been, for Mr. and Mrs. Davis – Agnes' father Wilson, and her mother Ethel – were both perfectly pleasant, relaxed, and welcoming.

It was Agnes' younger sisters who were the trouble.

"So, was it love at first sight, you two?" the three girls chirped the moment Agnes and RG walked in.

Fluttering around in the foyer, the sisters – Naomi, Vallie Lee and Clara – peppered RG with all sorts of questions (What was it like living on a farm? Did he ride horses? Was he a cowboy? How much did cows poop anyhow?) before launching into a series of embarrassing childhood stories about their sister, at which point Agnes promptly ended the conversation by hooking RG's arm and dragging him out the door, telling her family she wanted to show him around town.

"You think they were tolerant of me?" he asked as they walked down the sidewalk.

"Oh, more than tolerant," she said, and she took him forward by the arm.

She held onto him as they went. Down the street they walked, RG taking in the view of the quaint town with its small roads and little shops, the occasional automobile passing by, little kids peddling on bicycles behind them. He could imagine what Agnes must have been like all those years ago, just another kid growing up in town, her three younger sisters hanging at her hip as she led them to the grocery store, or the park, or the stretch of trees beyond. And it was as RG was imagining this scene that Agnes came to a stop.

Only now did she let go of his arm.

They had paused on the sidewalk in front of an empty lot in the middle of the road. It was an odd site in an otherwise charming district. Farther up the road were other shops and homes, just as there were more shops behind from whence they'd came, but here was nothing at all, like a gap from a lost tooth. People passing by barely seemed to notice this sad lot, as if it were invisible to them. The ground was patchy with weeds and dead grass, broken bottle shards glinting in the sunlight. Rocks lay here and there, but the rest was a kind of dull sand.

Ash, RG realized.

Then he realized what this place was.

Agnes had told him the story in one of her letters a few weeks earlier, but it was different to see it in person, to stand at the spot where her father's general store had once stood. There was nothing left of it now, not even a few charred bricks. The fire had devoured the building whole.

Of all RG had learned about Agnes so far, the story of her father's general store had seemed especially cruel. Like so many others, Agnes' family had struggled during the worst years of the Depression, but they had also felt an obligation to help. Men with hangdog faces would show up here at her father's store with heads bowed in shame, having no way to feed their families, and Agnes' father had allowed them all to buy what they needed on credit. They were his neighbors, his friends. They had hungry kids at home. But soon the credit piled up so high, Wilson Davis knew he wouldn't get his money back. Yet he kept giving more and more.

And to reward him for his generosity, fate had burned down his store.

There was no explanation for the fire, no obvious cause or culprit. A spark in the wind, a faulty electrical wire — none could say. He'd had no enemies anywhere. But with his debts and all his stock burned up in the fire, there was no money left to rebuild. Agnes' father had cleaned up the debris, hauling off in wagons the last remains of his life's work, and had then found a meager desk job working for the Rockingham County Farm Bureau. The spot of his old store had sat empty ever since.

A cold wind disturbed the ashen dust over the vacant lot, Agnes' dress ruffling and settling again. She was silent for now. Standing beside her, RG knew they were both looking at two different things – he at this sad vacant lot, and she at the store that had once stood here. He couldn't see the brick front of the store with its sturdy roof, nor the flag that had always hung from the same spot in its brass mount. He couldn't see the items on display in the window, which her father had always carefully arranged to catch the attention of those walking by. He couldn't see the front door, with its familiar clanging bell, nor could he walk through that door and browse the shelves of items, the bins of tool, the boxes of fabrics and the barrels of candy for the kids, all of which lived on as a memory, a ghost. But RG knew Agnes could see it all right there in front of her, her whole childhood overlaying the gray and scarred ground.

He also knew she was telling him something.

Now that she'd brought him here and revealed this part of herself to him, he realized he couldn't put if off much longer.

Soon, very soon, he would have to show her where he was from.

He would have to take her to the mountains.

CHAPTER 5

✦✦✦

All his life, RG had always figured he'd end up one day marrying a farmer's daughter from the mountains, someone accustomed to the lifestyle the farm demands, because who else would ever want to move to the mountains with him? Who else would be comfortable around stinky hogs and cattle?

Agnes, in her fancy dresses?

He was kidding himself. The past few months he'd been fooling her with his coat and tie look. He'd sat in the theatre and listened to violins and Tchaikovsky. Once she actually saw his home, though, she'd think twice.

But there was no getting around it, and if it wasn't going to work out between them, well, he figured let it be sooner rather than later.

So he took her to the farm in early April, 1941. Agnes was dressed up pretty in the passenger seat of his Pontiac, RG navigating the winding gravel backroads that rose and fell, climbing steadily, on their way to his land in Watauga County.

He could've picked a better time of year for a first impression. As the mountains rose closer and closer, the sunlight illuminating the muddy slopes, it seemed only to highlight their gloominess. This time of year, between winter and spring, was what native Wataugans called "mud season." The colors of the landscape were brown and gray. It was cold but not snowy, which was a shame. When it snowed the mountains were beautiful, frosted with shades of blue and white that glimmered blindingly in all directions, a winter wonderland like something from a children's fairy tale. The trees would freeze in place like glass figurines, ballerinas pirouetting down the slopes. Now, the trees looked more like gnarled skeletons rising out of the slop. Naked growth bent over the road as if they had the bad backs of old men, annoyed at being awoken from their slumbers. If he could've only waited until spring, when the flowers and canopies bloomed, when life began anew.

RG lived in a brick two-story farmhouse at the foot of hilly farmland in the valley under the mountains. When they arrived and parked the car in the puddled drive, he wasn't sure what to expect.

Agnes stepped out of the passenger side in her flower-patterned dress, wearing her nice gloves, and stood there for a moment, before walking carefully in her stylish shoes over soggy grass, beyond the stink of the hogs gorging from the trough nearby. The cattle were up higher in the hills, like statues, a few lifting their heads now and then but otherwise still. She held her hand over her eyes to regard them in the sunshine.

RG's eyes, meanwhile, were on her the whole time. Agnes looked so out of place — a colorful, exotic bird on a plot of mud. He was certain she would fly away on the spot.

Still, he gave her the grand tour. He showed her the old barn, the meat house, the spring house, the icehouse, the fields. And then he took her back up to the brick house. It probably wasn't well-decorated by her standards. Or anyone's standards, for that matter. RG never did have an eye for that.

They walked around the bland kitchen and living room, the smell of stale old wood left in the fireplace's hearth. Nothing to write home about. He also gave her fair warning as they walked up the stairs to the second floor, explaining how the ceiling wasn't quite finished. RG's Uncle Huston had left him this house after he'd died some years earlier. It was a sudden death, another sad story, but it also meant the house hadn't been fully completed. Whenever he wasn't working elsewhere, RG was doing his best to fix it up.

The roof was his current project. Upstairs, sunlight streamed in through the gaps in the ceiling. RG thought he should've at least called ahead to tell the farm workers to put a tarp over the roof before she came by to see it. Wasn't supposed to rain for a week, but still.

Downstairs again, Agnes walked through the rooms, nodding at this and that, and then she emerged back out on the porch, taking in the fresh air, looking out at all the land, the soft peaks of the Blue Ridge spread out in the distance.

He figured this was it. She was about to tell him they should get in the car, that they should go back. He wouldn't have blamed her.

But then, he noticed her pause there at the top of the porch steps, like a person at the edge of a diving board, and ever so slowly, she began sliding off her gloves.

"This would be a fine spot for a garden," she said, pointing down at the messy, muddy ground in the yard. "Don't you think?"

He hadn't thought of it, not at all.

But he found himself nodding his head as Agnes stepped off the porch, nodding even more now as she bent down and touched the dirt with her smooth fingers, feeling the mushy soil, letting it coat her hand.

PART TWO

MOUNTAIN BOY

CHAPTER 6

✦❦✦

When Agnes arrived at RG's farm in the High Country of North Carolina for the first time, she had to admit the place did seem to exist as its own world. Seeing the clouds rolling up the mountain peaks, the valley shrouded in ocean-thick fog, was like dozing off and slipping into a dream.

Only she wasn't dreaming for long – the roads were far too bumpy for that.

She soon found herself sitting, or bouncing really, in the passenger seat of RG's Pontiac as the vehicle lurched and rattled, tires spinning up dust, the two of them careening up and down roads that had been carved haphazardly through the mountains. Now that she'd seen the farm, he wanted to give her a tour of the rest of the county, dangerous cliffsides and all. Once or twice the vehicle tilted so severely on an uneven spot, Agnes thought they'd go rolling on down the mountain.

RG, though, was the picture of relaxation as he drove, casually pointing out landmarks through the valley, providing her with a brief overview of the area's history, as if they weren't taunting death with every bend in the road.

For generations, he told her, Watauga County and the surrounding area had been one of the so-called "lost provinces" of North Carolina, because it'd been impossible to reach by trains or roads. Separated from rest of the state by the Eastern Continental Divide — those mountainous ridges that rise up 3,000 feet and, like a knife blade, slice the running rainwater in two directions — the joke was that the only way to get to Watauga was to be born here. Anyone else would've had to hike on foot, the same way the early explorers had done.

But even now, Agnes found the roads weren't much – just gravel and dirt and loose rocks that rolled precariously down the slopes. Her ankles crossed on top of the rumbling car floor mats, she held her breath as they whipped around yet another cliffside.

It was impossible not to flinch every time.

Just when she was about to start worrying, they crested the hill in RG's Pontiac, and a full panorama of the mountains rose into view before them. Spread over the horizon, the rounded mountain peaks appeared to dive out of the clouds like so many humped back whales, frozen in time before they splashed back down again into the misty froth. The view was colossal, Biblical. It was as if she and RG were seated inside a small boat, surrounded by the most massive ocean waves God could form, bobbing at the highest point on the skyline.

For a moment, Agnes was speechless.

She'd never experienced anything quite like it.

Dutch Creek Falls, just a short horse ride from the house in which RG grew up.

CHAPTER 7

O ver the coming months, as winter began to thaw and the sound of birdsong and dripping tree canopies filled the valley, Agnes made multiple trips back to the farm with RG, occasionally for practical reasons, but mostly just to get away for a day.

And it really did feel *away* – away from the rest of the world. Away from the chaos of newspaper headlines and radio broadcasts about the war overseas. Away from reports of firebombs and charred European cities. Away from the draft and more American boys being enlisted in the armed forces.

RG's farm was in the town of Vilas, although maybe "town" wasn't exactly the right word for it, at least not compared to Agnes' hometown. Vilas had nothing more than a tiny post office to mark its spot on the local maps. Otherwise, it was just a collection of open fields and hills, tree-bordered graveyards and quiet streams, hidden ponds and animal burrows, designated a town not so much by signs or fencing, but rather by the inherited knowledge of the families that had always lived here.

All around Watauga were other small communities of that ilk: Sugar Grove, Zionville, Deep Gap, Bamboo, Matney, Sherwood, Foscoe, Shulls Mills, Meat Camp, Aho.

The names called to mind old tribes, each with its own passed-down history.

As for the story behind the county's name, "Watauga," Agnes learned that was a mystery, lost to time. Some claimed it was

Farmers threshing wheat in the traditional manner in the mountains of Watauga County.

a Cherokee word for "beautiful flowing waters," but you'd be hard-pressed to find any real Cherokee who'd tell you that was so. Others thought it referred to the great warrior tribe of Watauga Indians, although no such tribe was ever recorded to have existed. Still others thought it came from the language of a long-lost native people and that it meant, simply, "the land beyond." Agnes could have gone around the county knocking on doors and asking for the story, and no doubt each family would've had their own sure answer behind the name's origin, what their granddaddy or grandma had told them. It could mean "river of plenty" or "whispering waters" or "the land in the clouds" and on and on. But at the end of the day, the evidence for any of those explanations was as foggy as the mountain air itself.

What was known for sure was that the first documented white men to appear in Watauga had been Moravian missionaries, who arrived from Pennsylvania in 1752, seeking a new spot for a settlement. The legendary pioneer Daniel Boone, after whom the county's biggest town was later named, traveled through the area on hunting trips beginning about 17 years later in 1769. More weary settlers arrived in the coming decades: English, Germans, Scotts, Irish. Arrowheads found in the soil and Native artwork the early settlers dug up from the ground proved that Cherokees had once dominated this land, but they were ghosts now, only their bones remaining deep beneath the loam, the cause of their disappearance yet another local mystery.

More than 160 years after the first white man arrived in Watauga, RG was born on a farm in the small town of Valle Crucis at the banks of the Watauga River. He was the second youngest of seven children. His father, Ed Shipley, was a cattleman, renowned amongst his peers for having brought the first registered Hereford bulls into the state of North Carolina a few decades earlier. RG's mother, Minnie Lee Shipley, was a tough but kind-hearted Methodist who managed the farm while her husband was away on those long cattle drives, which she did while keeping RG and his six siblings fed and looked after.

Because his father was gone so often, and because his mother was always so busy, RG spent most of his childhood afternoons riding his pony across the valley to the farm of his father's brother, Huston Shipley. Uncle Huse, as RG called him, was in the cattle business too, and he knew more about animals than anyone RG had ever met. Huston didn't have children of his own, but in his nephew he'd found a willing apprentice, although from the moment he could talk, RG swore he'd never be a cattleman himself. Instead, he wanted to be a veterinarian. He told his uncle he would open an office in the valley one day, just down the way from the farm, where he would spend his life healing sick and injured animals, not raising them for slaughter. Uncle Huse told him that was a fine idea.

"My uncle was a progressive fellow," RG told Agnes many years later. "He had taken some special interest in me, for some reason."

But to become a skilled vet, RG had a lot to learn, so Huston

A scene from a farm in Watauga County, photographed when RG was a boy.

RG's father Ed Shipley, middle, was a stoic and severe man, accustomed to long silences out in the fields with his Herefords.

began schooling his nephew in the fine art of animal psychology. First, he taught RG how to read the animals, what attributes to look for – the angle of the neck, the thickness of the hindquarters, the shape of the face. Words like "phenotype" and "conformation" flowed off his uncle's tongue like magical spells. Huston would walk in slow circles around the cattle, reading their personalities through the smallest of gestures. The turn of one's head told him: *This one is aggressively protective of her calf, so best be careful around her.* The nudge of another's rear end as it munched on the grass translated to: *This one is relaxed, docile enough to pet if you like.* Huston knew from the jostling of the legs which of the cattle were dominant and which were submissive, which were guarded and which were outgoing, and he seemed to do all this without even thinking, as natural as blinking or breathing. As natural as the fog in the valley.

More than anything, RG wanted to be able to see like that one day.

CHAPTER 8

T he way Agnes heard him tell it all those years later, RG's childhood was cleaved in two.

There was "before," and then there was "after."

All that came "before" was like something out of a children's book. Pony rides up the mountains. Lessons with his uncle in the pasture. Chasing after baby calves. Sunsets painting warm golden light over the mountains.

Everything that came "after" – well, that's when RG usually got quiet.

He was 11 years old when his family lost the farm. One foggy morning, his father led him outside, lifted RG up from under his armpits and dropped him down in the back of a wagon piled with crates. His siblings crawled in the wagon around him and sat crammed together with their arms wrapped around their knees, and without even a few words of explanation, his family rode out of Watauga for good. RG didn't even know what was happening as he watched the mountains disappear behind them.

Even two decades later, when Agnes asked him about it, RG still didn't give too many details.

"My father was shortsighted," was about all he would say.

A bad investment. That was the short version of the story. Some cattleman friends had asked RG's father to co-sign a loan so they could start their own cattle operation, but Ed Shipley hadn't done his due diligence, and when his friends' business failed, the bank came to Ed for the money. It didn't take long for the score to be settled. As RG's family rode off in silence, strangers drove up to the farmhouse, like an invasive species, and began selling it off limb by limb.

"It was a pretty sad story there for awhile," RG told Agnes.

After losing the farm, the Shipleys crossed the border from North Carolina into Virginia, where they found a place to stop on the fringes of coal country, a town called Wallace. They moved into a log house with one floor. At night, the walls of the house let out high-pitched shrieks as the wind slid through gaps in the logs. The family was crammed together over cold, dusty floorboards. They scraped and pinched pennies to get by. RG spent his teenage years waking before dawn to deliver coal in a horse-drawn wagon. Most of his siblings took off to pursue new lives on their own. His mother fell silent and kept her eyes on the floorboards.

As for RG's father, Ed Shipley had gone from driving great migrations of cattle across the Shenandoah Valley, to delivering milk in a rickety old Ford truck to a bottling plant across town.

CHAPTER 9

✤

Years went by, and RG grew accustomed to the coal-grey skies and buzzcut hills. He did well in school, played catcher on the baseball team, his mitt stained black from the coal dust that seemed to permanently coat his hands. Every year, there were fewer boys in his class. They all dropped out to work. But RG kept his early morning delivery job and made sure to get to school on time, while also helping his father raise dairy cows when class let out.

He'd never given up on his childhood dream of returning to Watauga one day to run his own veterinary practice, and at least once a summer, with his father's permission, he hitchhiked his way back down into North Carolina to spend a few weeks on his Uncle Huston's farm.

Those summer visits were almost painfully beautiful. After being starved of color for so long, the lush green of the mountains and the wide expanse of ocean-blue sky were delicious.

With Huston he learned something new each day. They worked until their bodies ached. Then, in rocking chairs side by side, the two would sip sweet tea out on the porch as the evening rolled in, marinating the mountains in that golden Carolina sunset.

It was the only place RG ever felt he could fully breathe, fully exhale.

When he said goodbye to his uncle at the end of each summer, the journey back to Virginia was always disorienting, as if someone had just shaken him awake from a dream.

CHAPTER 10

⤞⚜⚜⤝

B y the time RG graduated from high school, he was one of just three boys remaining in his class. Through a gritty mixture of luck and resolve, he wound up getting accepted to attend the prestigious Virginia Polytechnic Institute in Blacksburg, Virginia, where he intended to study veterinary science.

After borrowing money from a local doctor for a bus ticket, he arrived with nothing more than a small bag – and nowhere to stay.

Right away, he felt out of place. Never mind that he probably smelled like coal dust and the rank perfume of his horse-drawn wagon. His clothes were patched and threadbare, his shoes barely holding together, while all around him wealthy-looking young men wearing crisp military uniforms went marching by, their polished buckles glinting in the mist. VPI was a school that functionated mainly as a prep-academy for those looking to enter the armed forces. RG had been given permission to attend as a "day student," meaning he was excused from the formations and drills. His job was to work in the school's dairy department, milking test cows by hand four times a day and keeping records. He would make sure the gleaming boys had milk to drink in the cafeteria. That was his role in the grand American experiment.

But he still needed a place to sleep, and at the last minute, he managed to find a room in an old widow's boarding house for $30 a month, breakfast and dinner included, which was lucky, considering he didn't have any money left over for food.

RG decided that was fine by him. He could get by without a

lunch for the year.

Soon, he wouldn't be the only one with an empty stomach. Just a few weeks after he arrived on campus, the American stock market collapsed, and newspapers reported as businesses and factories slowed down production and began firing workers nationwide. Confusing terms like "brokerage offices" and "margin traders" and "valuation tables" floated out of the radio, while stories began to spread of people forced to huddle in lines down city blocks just to get a loaf of bread or some watery soup.

RG felt lucky to have any job, but his schedule was arguably even more militaristic than those of the uniformed cadets on campus. He could sleep in as late as 5 a.m. each morning, but the moment he opened his eyes, he would have to scramble to get ready. He would get dressed, then begin the long process of putting his shoes together. Not putting his shoes *on*, no. Putting them *together*. The pair had finally given out on him a few weeks earlier, both shoes splitting apart at the soles over the course of a few days, and since he couldn't afford replacements, he started each day by wrapping binder twine around them over and over to keep them from falling apart off his feet, then tying a big ugly knot at the top, like a bow on the world's worst Christmas present.

Once he'd gotten dressed in the morning with his shoes snug on his feet, RG would scarf down some breakfast and race off to the dairy barn to milk the school's test cows. Although the dairy department had a milking machine on campus, they wanted all the test cows to be milked by hand, for some bureaucratic reason or another. Once that was done, RG would run to class, and immediately afterward he had to rush right back to the barn for the cows' next milking session. Then class again. Cows again. Class, cows. No lunch. And the rest of the day would be spent hunched over textbooks in the library, his stomach growling, before eating a quick dinner of bread and soup back at the boarding house, undoing his shoes and collapsing into bed at night, his hands clenching at invisible cow udders in his sleep.

Uncle Huston told him not to get discouraged. In letters that arrived every few days at RG's boarding house, Huston wrote about the farm back home and the latest news from the valley: all the people migrating out of the mountains and into the nearest cities to find work. Everyone was going through tough times. He told RG he was proud of him for making a life for himself.

RG and his uncle were always writing back and forth. Their letters were usually about nothing in particular, a catalogue of random news, livestock tidbits and comments about theology that likely would've intrigued no one but them.

But one night in early autumn, when RG returned dog-tired to the boarding house, he opened Huston's latest letter and was greeted by some unexpected news – an engagement announcement.

A beautiful Tennessee gal, Huston wrote. It was quite unexpected, he admitted, especially for him, but he told RG there were no two ways about it. It was true love. After all these years, Huston had finally found the one.

When Agnes heard this story years later, she was confused. Hadn't RG said his Uncle Huston had never married?

"He was getting married," RG explained.

In fact, wedding invitations were mailed out that very week after RG received Huston's letter. But that made it all even worse, RG told Agnes, because just a few weeks later, a sudden cold front swept over the mountains, the temperature falling 6 degrees below zero, freezing the valley and forcing Huston out into the wilderness to chop more firewood, working like a man possessed as he loaded a wagon high with logs, rushing back to the brick house to keep the fire going in the hearth, to keep the house warm at all costs.

But it was no use.

"He was getting married," RG told Agnes, "and his bride-to-be developed pneumonia and died."

Huston was "so taken" after that, he wrote to RG saying he knew he would never marry thereafter for the rest of his life.

Just that story by itself would've been sad enough to Agnes

The only known photo of Huston Shipley.

had it ended there. Because invitations had been mailed out, RG's uncle had been obligated to take the time to write to everyone explaining why the wedding had to be called off. To Agnes, the thought of that poor man having to sit down and write out his grief over and over again was enough to break her heart.

But the story did not end there.

On the night of December 18, 1929, just when the campus of VPI was getting ready to clear out for the Christmas holiday, RG returned to his boarding house to find a telegram from his father, which informed him, in just a few short sentences, that Huston was dead.

Funeral in two days, RG's father wrote. *Come to Vilas.*

RG woke early the next morning, packed his bag in a daze and hiked out to the main roadway off campus. Winter had arrived aggressively that year. Snow clung to his coat and biting wind mangled his collar as he hiked along, shivering, turning to raise an arm to the occasional passing motorist.

He had to hitchhike in the cold all the way back to Watauga for the funeral, a distance of 150 miles. Each time he got picked up, he did his best to act thankful and cheery, but the truth was he was numb.

The whole journey was a blur. No matter whether he was sitting in the passenger seat of a stranger's car or hiking along in the slush, RG just couldn't wrap his mind around it. His uncle had been so healthy and vigorous the last he'd seen him, even with the cold of the season. How could a man like that just slip away?

A broken heart, RG decided. That was the only possible explanation.

But that was not true.

It was just the only explanation he wanted to consider.

Snow gusts swirled and kept on swirling as he traveled farther south. It was the worst blizzard in years. The mountain newspaper, the *Watauga Democrat,* would later proclaim, "The streets were practically deserted throughout the day and with the heavy snowfall and accompanying wind, those who took their motors from their garages were soon baffled by the skidding tires and piercing cold."

Despite a good number of motorists taking pity upon him and stopping to pick him up, RG was the last in the family to arrive back in Watauga, so he was also the last to learn what had been discovered in Huston's will.

His family had all gathered inside Huston's brick house. RG was practically standing in the doorway, his hair frosted white and his cheeks red and raw, when they told him.

In his will, Huston had decided to leave everything — the barn, the meat house, the icehouse, the spring house, the Herefords, all 122 acres of wheat fields, pasture and hills, and the very brick house in which the whole family was now standing — *"to my nephew Robert Gray Shipley."*

RG was 17 years old.

CHAPTER 11

~~⚜~~

S omething inside RG changed after his uncle died, just as the whole country seemed to have changed in some deep-down, permanent way.

1930 – a new year, a new decade. Photographs of empty factories soon filled the front pages of newspapers. Newsreel clips showed men nailing "CLOSED" signs on the doors of shops, "NO HELP WANTED" posters glued to office windows.

"In the 1920s, the great American word was 'prosperity,'" one newsreel narrator declared. "Now the '30s have begun, and there is a new word: 'Depression.'"

As the bewildered nation staggered into a new decade, RG dealt with his own despair by working – working constantly. If before Huston's death his daily schedule had been exhaustive, now it bordered on insanity. At 17 years old, he was stubborn enough to believe he could still finish up college at VPI and one day become a veterinarian, while also running a farm 150 miles away.

Later, when she heard this story, Agnes asked him how he'd even managed to get back and forth between school and the farm so often. Did he take the bus? The train?

"No, no, I bummed," RG said. "I had this little satchel that had a Virginia Tech sticker on it, and you could get a ride, there was no problem. I could travel quicker by bumming than I could on the train or the bus or any other way," he added, and he laughed at that, as if this part of his life was a comedy and not a sad spell of loneliness.

Besides, he said, bumming was the only way to travel for free. "I didn't have the money in the first place," he told her.

There were plenty of Huston's old farm workers who lived on the land, who'd watched RG grow up, and who now did all they could to help him keep the place running, but RG's life in the early 1930s remained one of constant movement – sending telegrams to the farm workers for the latest updates, hitchhiking back and forth between VPI's campus and Watauga every few days, reading class textbooks while in the seats of strangers' automobiles, then drawing up breeding and crop schedules for the farm while sitting exhausted in class.

He rarely slept. There was no time for friends, no time for late nights or going out on the town. "That wasn't a major part of my life," RG later said. "I didn't get to go to any of the football games. I didn't go to any of the formal dances. I didn't have the money or the time. Why, I didn't have a spare minute hardly to speak."

When Agnes asked him if he'd had any fun at all during college, RG admitted, "Well... I would go to a movie maybe once every two or three months or something," as if that were some wild, guilty extravagance.

Otherwise, the only time he spent outside of the classroom or working on the farm were the occasional weekends he went on trips with the school's dairy judging team, which traveled all over the country for competitions. RG had joined the team on a whim, figuring it might be a good chance to hone his eye for animals. His first year, at the season-end contest in St. Louis, Missouri, RG won second place in the nation.

Had she known him back in those days, Agnes would've told him his obsessiveness about everything he did was arguably unhealthy, but RG had managed to convince himself he was fine. There was nothing wrong with not sleeping, he told himself. Nothing wrong with working 18-hour days, seven days a week. Nothing wrong with isolating himself from other people.

"Oh, it wasn't so bad," was how he summed it up.

By graduation, RG had completed enough classes to earn himself three degrees – one in dairy science, one in animal husbandry, and one in agricultural education – although the school administrators later called him into a back office and informed him that he would only be allowed to accept one degree – because, they said, handing out three diplomas to one student wouldn't fit very well with the image of a school as academically rigorous as VPI, now would it?

Judging by his tone as he told that story years later, Agnes could tell RG was still a little mad about that.

Upon graduation, he planned to enroll straight away in a doctoral program to become a veterinarian, but with the Depression still choking his finances, he couldn't afford tuition.

"There wasn't any extra money to pay for anything else," he said. Finding a job was no easy task either. "Employment was so hard to come by, it was so scarce. But they were employing teachers some. I didn't have any other opportunities."

He accepted a year-long teaching position at the Patterson School in Lenoir, North Carolina, instructing boys in an old schoolhouse heated by a woodstove through winter, and when that gig was up, he heard another temporary teaching position had just become available at the high school in Boone, just down the road from his farm in Vilas.

"The present teacher was wanting to retire," RG later said. "They asked me if I would take the job and I told them, no, that I planned to go back to school and study veterinary medicine in September. But if they wanted me to, I would fill out the rest of the year for them."

He couldn't say, later on, whether he'd known how difficult it would be for him to leave once he moved back home for good.

CHAPTER 12

❦

As a child, RG had gotten to know the mountains on long pony rides, exploring the ancient wilderness, the cold bubbling creeks and wide open cliffsides, back when summer lasted a thousand years.

Now that he'd returned to Watuaga as a young man in his early 20s to live full-time, he got to know his home again in the evening and early morning hours, driving his Pontiac up and down the hills, visiting families all over the valley.

Technically, these visits weren't a part of his job at all. As the new vocational agriculture teacher at the high school – and a self-avowed temporary one at that – RG's only responsibility was to guide his students. But whenever folks around Watauga had trouble on their farms – hogs dropping dead, soil gone barren, a sheep going through tough labor – he couldn't help but offer up his expertise. RG would then navigate the hills and arrive on their doorstep in coat and tie, bag of tools in hand, like a country doctor making house calls.

"I felt like it was my responsibility if I could," he later told Agnes.

Soon the name "Robert Gray Shipley" became a running topic of conversation among the farmers who'd gather inside Mast General Store while collecting their mail, and when RG stopped in to stock up on supplies, they all went silent as he passed by the potbelly stove. It was rumored the young Mr. Shipley knew more about animal science, soil chemistry, dairy science, and agriculture than just about anyone else in the state.

Thencamethestoriesthatappearedonthefrontpageofthe *Watauga Democrat* that summer, after RG's first year of teaching was up. As it happened, instead of getting ready to leave to study veterinary medicine as he'd originally planned, RG decided to do the most logical alternative: organize a 4,000-mile cross-country road trip for his entire class of students, more than 20 high school boys altogether.

News of the so-called "Southwestern Tour" was so unusual, so fantastical, that the *Watauga Democrat* plotted their journey for the whole county to follow. It was height of the Great Depression, and people needed something hopeful in their lives, a common cause to rally behind, a distraction. "They expect to leave Monday, June 1," the paper told its readers on the front page of the May 28, 1936, edition, "and go down through the Tennessee Valley and cross the Mississippi River at New Orleans, thence to old Mexico and return to the Centennial Exposition at Dallas. On the return trip the group will go through Oklahoma, Kansas, Illinois, Indiana, Kentucky and Virginia."

When the boys finished their trip weeks later, they returned to the mountains in the truck bed of a '38 Chevy with stories right out of a boy's paperback adventure novel. Canoe rides down the mighty Mississippi. Dust bowl towns abandoned like lost ruins. Jazzy nights in New Orleans. Shrimp boat excursions on the Gulf. Most of these boys had never even stepped foot over the county line of Watauga before, and now they weaved tales of trains wailing through the long prairie nights of the Midwest. They'd wandered through hazy markets on the Mexican border, and they'd dipped canoe oars into the placid waters of the Ohio River. They'd even met the president himself, Franklin Delano Roosevelt, while he was at a campaign stop at that summer's Centennial World's Fair in Dallas, Texas. Wearing a snow-white suit, the president had been seated up in the back of an open-air limonene, which happened to crawl to a stop at the street corner right beside the group of mountain boys. None of them had even known the president was in town. They would've

The installation of the electrical lines spanned the mountainous ridges and the dips in the valley.

reached out to shake his hand had they not been so stunned. Roosevelt just smiled and waved at them, his limo then carrying him forward in the summer haze.

The southwestern trip turned RG into a household name across the county, but he made even bigger headlines the following autumn, soon after his 24th birthday, when he helped bring light to the mountains.

That September, around the same time he began his second year at the high school, the Rural Electrical Administration in Washington DC sent representatives down to Watauga to see about setting up electrical infrastructure in the valley. It was one of Roosevelt's New Deal initiatives. But at those first community meetings, the DC folks didn't exactly receive a warm welcome. What with how wary mountain folks could be of outsiders, especially outsiders who proposed stabbing strange wooden poles into their land and stringing dangerous wires inside their homes where their children slept, it was a tough sell. But RG had read the reports, had attended all the meetings, and had listened closely, so he took it upon himself to go around the county, house by house, and personally vouch for the importance of the electrification project, while also drawing out detailed maps for where the transmission lines should be installed to most benefit the residents. His efforts caught the attention of North Carolina Congressman Bob Doughton, the chairman of the powerful House Ways and Means Committee, who, just a year prior, had stood on the right-hand side of President Roosevelt during the signing of the Social Security Act, and who now appeared at the brick house in Vilas to personally congratulate RG for his efforts. The local civil engineer, Mr. Richard Olsen, also thanked RG on the front page of the paper for having "laid aside usual duties and gone into the field to secure the detailed information required... The type of cooperation shown," Olsen added, "is of the most unselfish and valuable kind."

RG continued to teach for another three years in Watauga County, while spending his summer breaks completing a master's degree piecemeal. He would've preferred earning his doctorate to become a veterinarian, but the programs were not nearly as flexible, and he figured a master's degree was as good a first step as any.

By the time RG finally left his job at the high school, four years later than he'd originally planned, Watauga County was transformed. By day, it looked just about the same. Observant travelers passing through might have spotted the new electrical lines snaking through the hills, but for the most part they blended in with the trees. It was only when night fell that the heavy shroud of darkness, once so formidable, was softly bombarded all over by the nocturnal emergence of light, like so many moons blooming at once. 300 miles of electrical lines had been installed, servicing 2,400 homes. Through the black fog of evening, one could see the glow of illuminated windows. All over the valley, electrified homes hummed past nightfall. Silhouettes passed by in the windows now: women cooking beans and lard in iron pans, grandmas reading to children in wooden chairs, men smoking pipes of burley tobacco, girls and boys shuffling in play over the floorboards.

And years later, on warm Spring nights in 1941, RG and Agnes would be able to dance in the illuminated living room of his brick house, the radio playing Frank Sinatra as the crickets sang along through the valley.

CHAPTER 13

O nly Agnes ever saw him dance.

What she loved most of all were those cool spring evenings, listening to the radio with him on the farm, music filling the once-lonely rooms of the brick house.

Their favorite radio program was "The Hit Parade," which aired all over the country, showcasing live performances of the top hits from the most popular musicians of the day.

That was how Agnes and RG first heard the song, what soon became *their* song: "Night and Day," sung by Frank Sinatra.

Night and day...
You are the one.
Only you... neath the moon...
Or under the stars...

Whenever it came on at the brick house that spring, they'd sway back and forth between the chairs over the old rug in the living room. RG's muddy boots sat by the door, so he danced in his socks, while the radio crackled like logs in a fireplace.

Whether near to me or far...
No matter, darling, where you are...
I think of you...
Day and night...
Night and day...

And this man of hers, who could dance to a sweet song on the radio, would then have to slide his boots back on and head out to feed the cattle and dump the slop for the hogs.

Agnes never minded that part of him.

The truth was, she liked it.

She'd been back to the farm enough times that she'd begun to feel at home out here in the mountains, although she still hadn't learned to wear more suitable shoes. That was a lesson she simply refused to learn. Instead, she'd become quite skillful at walking over any farm terrain in her stylish shoes, taking care to clean them off properly whenever she stepped back inside.

Besides, there was work for her to get done. While RG was out tending to the farm, she did her best to fix up the house. Beyond nailing in rafters on the ceiling or prying out old floorboards, there were plenty of small touches that did wonders. A well-placed vase of flowers could transform a room. A rug here, some curtains there. A good polishing of the banisters to give the good old wood some of its original shine back.

She never stayed the night, of course – that wouldn't have been proper – but their visits did tend to stretch on a bit longer as the weather warmed. Usually on these starlit nights, while RG was out feeding the cattle before they drove back to Virginia, she would switch on the radio in the living room and let the sound float into the kitchen as she fixed them up something quick and easy for dinner.

By this late in the day, "The Hit Parade" broadcast would be replaced by news about the fighting overseas. The countless deaths, the cities burned. Talk of the war had been dominating conversation for months. Out here in the mountains, at least, it was easier to put out of mind.

As the radio played, Agnes would move about the kitchen without thinking, no longer having to open random cupboards and search around in drawers to find what she needed to get a meal together. She already knew the homes for his various pots, pans and ingredients, even if RG had no clue most of the time.

Honestly, the man seemed utterly incapable of feeding himself.

"How did you manage to get this far in life without starving to death?" she had asked him a few weeks earlier, and he'd just shrugged and grinned as she'd pried a pan loose from a chaotic jumble of random items in the cabinet.

What made it so odd was that in many ways, RG was somewhat of a genius.

It had come as a gradual shock when she'd realized just how formidably his mind worked, what with how aloof he could act sometimes. RG's power of recall alone was extraordinary. Any town he had ever visited, even if he'd only driven through it once years ago, he could sit down on the spot and draw an accurate map of its layout, right down to the locations of shops, banks, restaurants, light posts and that gnarled curve of the tree trunk where he'd taken a left-hand turn. Phone numbers and addresses too might as well have been carved into stone in his head, the way he could rattle them off so easily. The smallest of details about a person he'd met, a newspaper article he'd read a few months back, the radio program he'd heard three Christmases ago: It was all stored permanently in his mind.

But nothing compared to how deeply he understood his animals. Even from a distance, RG could distinguish between the cattle by seemingly invisible differences in their silhouettes. He could read sickness in an animal by a sluggish blink of its eyes, could sense unease through the small furrow of one's ears. It was astounding.

And this same man, this genius, couldn't even fry up a couple of eggs to save his life.

Over the last few months, Agnes had gotten to see him interact with other people who lived in the mountains, and it was funny how different he was to them. Out there in the community, in his coat and tie, he was always "Mr. Shipley," the respected teacher, landowner and community advocate, a county agent with a master's degree worth of knowledge who might soon earn a doctoral degree to become a celebrated veterinarian.

But here in the brick house, alone with her, he was always "Bob."

That's what she called him, at least.

Early on, he had begun calling her by a sweet pet name, "Sadie," derived from the Hebrew word for "princess," which he'd found by parsing through the Old Testament and coming upon what he thought was a particularly fitting passage to describe her beauty.

And in response to that researched show of admiration, she'd stuck with "Bob."

Just that: "Bob."

Of all the other possible iterations of his name — "Robert," "Robert Gray," "RG," "Mr. Shipley" — she thought "Bob" suited him best.

That was the man he was to her.

The window was open now, a cool evening breeze wafting into the kitchen. May of 1941 had arrived in the mountains a week earlier, and with it came the smell of freshly plowed soil. The breeze and the damp fragrance swirled with the voices of the radio broadcasters in the kitchen as Agnes stood over the counter, slicing some tomatoes over an old wooden cutting board.

They had to get back on the road soon. After cutting the tomatoes, she arranged the slices atop some bread, with cheese and country ham, then rinsed the knife under the faucet. Meanwhile, the radio broadcasters were discussing the odds of the USA entering the war. After the passage of the Lend-Lease Act, which had formally authorized the USA to ship supplies — food and oil, but also warships and warplanes — to the British and other Allied nations, it seemed like the country had finally picked a side.

"We are pledged to give all out-aid to Britain," read a story in the May 8, 1941, issue of the *Watauga Democrat,* which had arrived in RG's mailbox that morning. "The people favor our stand as the 'arsenal of democracy.' ...We must take any steps necessary."

Drying her hands, Agnes went into the living room, switched off the radio and went to go call RG in to eat. As she stepped out on the porch, she could just make out his silhouette along the fence line by the Herefords. He was holding up his lantern, tossing light back and forth over the animals. RG's face was illuminated as he lifted the lantern to inspect them. The animals' white faces and curved horns glowing in the dark gave them the appearance of mythical creatures.

As for RG, he looked almost gentle, hoisting his light, speaking softly to each animal in turn. She could see in moments like this the veterinarian he'd always wanted to be – a ghost version of himself from another life. He was still young, and he still had time to complete a doctoral degree, but a part of her knew that dream of his might never happen. Even his master's degree and his job as a county agent had begun to seem like a diversion, a detour. She knew what his Uncle Huston had known long ago, why the man had left his nephew this land in the first place.

RG's home was here. Always had been.

Agnes gripped the worn wooden railing of the porch. There was still so much she was figuring out in her life, but the notion that some fighting going on overseas would make its way here, to this cattle farm in the Blue Ridge Mountains, seemed, to her, impossible.

If Watauga was its own world, let it stay that way.

PART THREE

FLIGHT

CHAPTER 14

❦

I n October of 1942, the movie "Flying Tigers" was showing in theaters all over the country. RG and Agnes caught a showing of it at the Appalachian Theatre in downtown Boone, North Carolina, the only theatre for miles, on one of their trips back to Watauga.

Girls from the nearby Appalachian Teachers College were gathered in a flock of white skirts and braided hair under the gleaming mint green façade of the theatre. RG put his arm around Agnes' waist, navigating them through the crowd, and paid at the window, 75 cents for two adult tickets and a bucket of popcorn.

Inside the theatre, they settled into their seats as the lights dimmed.

The movie starred John Wayne, who played the leader of a ragtag group of independent, volunteer pilots flying combat missions against Japan in the weeks after the surprise Japanese attack at Pearl Harbor, which had finally catapulted the United States into the war.

"Flying Tigers" was what they called a "flagwaver film," the kind of movie that would get people punching their armrests, stomping the floor, spilling their popcorn.

The US has been formally at war with Germany and Japan for nearly a year when the movie premiered, which also happened to be the same week RG and Agnes had planned for their wedding. All over the country, boys were enlisting or already training to fight. RG had been deferred from the draft because of his job as a county agent. The federal government had wanted him and the other agents to remain temporarily stateside to ensure the durability of the agricultural supply chain, but in the coming weeks that would likely change.

They expected 90 days, tops.

Sitting in the theatre with her fiancé, watching those airplanes get ripped apart by bullets, the debris of scattered popcorn all around her, Agnes knew it was only a matter of time.

CHAPTER 15

᠊᠊᠊᠊᠊᠊᠊᠊᠊᠊᠊᠊

They held the wedding ceremony a few days later in Agnes' hometown at the McGaheysville Methodist Church at 4 p.m. Saturday, October 10, 1942.

Agnes wore a simple but elegant green woolen crepe dress and a beautiful corsage of orchid and stephanotis flowers, which she'd made herself.

RG, keeping it simple, wore his regular coat and tie.

After the ceremony they gathered for the reception at Agnes' childhood home, a small crowd in the living room, eating homemade cake for which everyone had donated ration cards in order get enough sugar. It was mostly just Agnes' side of the family and some old school friends of hers. RG, the mountain boy, was outnumbered. Only his mother and one of his sisters had been able to make it. The rest of his family was too scattered across the country. RG didn't blame them for not making it to the wedding. It wasn't as if he'd given them a whole lot of notice ahead of time.

Besides, there was a war going on. Everyone was getting married. "Til death do us part" could be right around the bend.

CHAPTER 16

The honeymoon began right away, RG and Agnes setting off on a trip deeper South. He'd saved up enough ration cards for the gas. They planned to stay for a spell in Charleston, South Carolina, then hop on a steamer in Savannah, Georgia, and travel by rail into Tampa, Florida, where RG's baby brother Joe was stationed as a test pilot at the MacDill Air Force Base.

Driving down the backroads, they watched the mountains flatten, the landscape soften and the loamy North Carolina soil lighten to a fine yellow sand that dusted the sides of the South Carolina roadway. Shacks, restaurants and general stores leaned out from the overgrowth. Tin signs beckoned travelers to stop for the best Frogmore stew, oysters and hoppin' John, while inns advertised clean rooms. Palmetto trees spiked their palms out in the humid air like shaggy dogs. They'd entered the Lowcountry. With the windows down, the smell of the ocean lapped into the Pontiac, and they breathed it in.

Charleston, when they arrived, was far livelier than they could've anticipated. The first thing they saw as they entered the city proper was a hulking boat crawling slowly along the coastline. They rolled down their windows to see over the side of the bridge. It looked to be some kind of party. Men were cheering on the ship, waving their arms, riding that great metal beast like a sedated whale as tugboats towed it gently along the waterway. Later in the day Agnes and RG learned from a native Charlestonian that what they'd seen had been a tank-landing ship, one of a few that had just emerged from the Charleston navy yard. Those boys had been celebrating its departure.

"Charleston is a lovely old town," Agnes later wrote her family, "and we didn't have nearly enough time there."

They would've needed weeks to savor the full breadth of the banquet before them. Everywhere they went in that lush port city, the atmosphere was excited and bloated by the war, as if all of Charleston had stuffed itself too quickly with the bounty of it all and was now suffering from indigestion. Military folks filled the streets, their vehicles honking and zooming all around. Older women stuffed into tight dresses sauntered like plump turkeys past skinny boys in loose-fitting uniforms. Advertisements along the streets warned people not to make long distance phone calls so as not to hold up the lines for vital communications from war industry and military personnel. In that evening's edition of the *Charleston News and Courier*, an ad promoting the laxative capabilities of Kellogg's All-Bran cereal ran with the unfortunate headline, "Here's how I licked wartime constipation!"

Agnes and RG, dazed by the chaos of it all, tried countless places but couldn't for the life of them manage to get a hotel room. All the hotel space, they were informed, had been confiscated at the last minute for the war effort.

They ended up finding a small room in one of the old colonial homes in the city's sequestered French Quarter.

"It was worth it for the delay," Agnes wrote. "We stayed in one of those lovely old homes you read about. The entire house was antique high ceilings, and our room was just like a picture. A four-poster bed with a canopy and everything... such luxury."

By now it was late. The city was quieting down. Agnes opened the window in their room as the autumn breeze flapped the curtains, and she looked out at the narrow, cobbled streets below, the pastel homes the colors of Easter eggs, palm trees chaperoning over the slanted townhome rooftops. It was easy to imagine they were back in Revolutionary War times. Small fires flickered in glass boxes at each doorway, casting warm shadows as night fell. The sound of clopping horse carriages lulled against the gentle roar of faraway engines. Beyond the rooftops was the ocean, and somewhere over the horizon, under the vastness of the stars, the same boat they'd seen earlier in the day was drifting far out to sea, carrying those boys to a place none of them should be going.

Agnes closed the curtains.

CHAPTER 17

＊＊＊

6 6 Tuesday night we drove on to Savannah, Georgia, left our
car there and hopped on board the steamliner, went to bed
and woke up in Tampa, Florida," Agnes wrote to her family.
"You know I have never ridden a train of that sort much less
slept in a Pullman."

They felt like fancy rich folks as they stepped out of the train
station in Tampa, only to be greeted by God's thunder from the
sky above.

Airplanes weaved and spiraled and sliced through clouds. It
was all people could talk about on the streets of Tampa from
the moment RG and Agnes began exploring the city. Every person they met, from small children to cane-hobbling old folk,
seemed to be amateur aviation experts, what with the Mac-
Dill Air Force Base being so close by. It had become their local
sports team, and they were all passionate fans. The locals could
distinguish the smallest differences between one airplane type
over another. At one point during RG and Agnes' exploration, a
blind man walked by with his dog and, as if sensing they were
tourists, stopped to explain the different airplanes by their
unique sounds, before tipping his hat and strolling off. "The
way he got along you would never have guessed he was blind,"
Agnes later wrote.

That night they got to see the Air Force base for themselves.
They met RG's brother Joe and his young bride Jocelyn at the
officer's club, amidst a throng of pilots and cigarette smoke.

RG's brother Joe Shipley graduated near the top of his class at
West Point and served among the most daring pilots in the nation.

Joe was exactly as Agnes had expected: charming, intelligent, and handsome in his pilot's uniform, looking like a young movie star. Still, if Joe had one blind spot (to use a pilot's term), it was his inability to fully see the girl clinging to his arm. No doubt Jocelyn was gorgeous. Blonde and thin, bouncing and giggling like a schoolgirl, she radiated the youthful beaty of an MGM starlet. But Agnes remembered something RG had once told her, about how his sisters didn't care for Jocelyn much, and the longer the girl kept on rambling and interrupting the conversation, Agnes couldn't help but agree.

But Joe was a pilot, after all, and what did pilots do? They painted pretty pinup girls on the sides of their airplanes. Evidently, he had a type.

Gritting her teeth, Agnes nodded along to whatever the girl said.

It was worth it to see RG and his brother together. She hadn't gotten the chance to spend much time with his family, and watching him grin and talk up his little brother, she saw a sweetness he usually kept hidden. John Wayne in that movie "Flying Tigers?" The way RG saw it, he had nothing on Joe, who flew the most amazing airplanes ever built, soaring the country into the future.

Somewhere between the dessert and the check, RG told a story about how when Joe was just a little kid, he'd always liked going out on pony rides up the mountains. Joe was too young to ride a pony of his own, so RG would have him sit with him, Joe's arms wrapped around RG's waist. Together, they'd go all the way up to the mountain peaks, looking out at the soft ripples of the Blue Ridge. The whole skyline was there. And who knows? Maybe that's what got Joe thinking about being a pilot in the first place. To see what lay beyond the horizon.

Later that night, as they departed under the lamppost light, Agnes heard RG tell his little brother how proud he was of him, and she heard Joe congratulate his older brother on finally getting married, calling him "an old man." The two shook hands and said they'd see each other real soon. They were still laughing and yelling back at each other as they went in different directions down the sidewalk.

When they got back to their hotel, Agnes wrote to her sisters, "Bob is sweeter each day if such is possible."

CHAPTER 18

RG's draft notice arrived in the mail a few weeks after the honeymoon.

They'd known it was coming, and yet the pace at which he was digested by the American military was still jarring.

He was promptly sent to boot camp, then on to mechanic's school, followed by gunnery school, where he was put to work teaching airmen how to operate the tail turret and 2-caliber mounted machine guns on the B-24 bomber. Part of his job was making sure his trainees could react quickly and effectively if something went wrong while they were up in the sky. It was all about assembling and disassembling, assembling and disassembling – looking for malfunctions, for things that weren't quite right, abnormalities that could lead to death in the sky. RG was serious about his job, and he drove his students hard. He told his boys he wanted them to know their weapons so well they could feel the malfunctions from touch alone. Skin upon metal, the vibrations telling them what they needed to know.

He didn't have much time to think about things back home. His father had gone back to Watauga to help look over his farm while he was gone, which was lucky, since RG's job as an instructor took him from city to city as the need arose, often at no more than a day's notice. Agnes was able to follow along with him. They moved eight times in eight weeks. They'd gotten used to barely even unpacking their suitcases when they reached a

RG pictured shortly after being drafted.

new destination.

By the spring of 1943, they were living in Laredo, Texas. They'd gotten a small apartment with the help of the orderly room folks on base – another lucky break, since most couples weren't able to live together. As far as things go, it wasn't so bad. RG got to eat dinner with Agnes every night. They shared the same bed. Woke up each morning and had breakfast together. Then off he went to contribute to that day's war effort, kissing her goodbye like a salesman off to go hawk vacuum cleaners. Agnes was just glad to have RG still with her and not overseas.

Still, it wasn't exactly luxurious, and it didn't help their egos that RG's baby brother Joe and his wife Jocelyn were living in high cotton down in Tampa.

Jocelyn wrote to Agnes from time to time, which was frustrating because Agnes felt obligated to respond, and the girl's letters were always a handful.

"We have a large home now with 4 bedrooms so we'll have lots of room if you all come visit," Jocelyn said in her last letter, which was postmarked March 30, 1943.

What really peeved Agnes was the way Jocelyn tried to couch her bragging in faux humility.

"Joe got his promotion and a wonderful new job," Jocelyn wrote, before making sure to add, "but he has so much responsibility + work we never have any time together!"

As for the fancy new house, Jocelyn said, "The house is so large and so much to take care of and we always have so much company," as if the prospect of looking after a mansion full of wonderful friends was deserving of Agnes' sympathy.

Then there was the big news, which Agnes delivered to RG that night by sliding him the letter over the dinner table.

"I'll let you in on our big secret," Jocelyn had written, "but don't dare tell it to a soul as we still want it to be a secret. There'll be an addition to this branch of the family in Oct. We're so happy we can't even see straight."

RG could only smile and shake his head, setting the letter

aside. "That's quite a sight about their 'addition,'" he told Agnes. "I too am envious of them. It sure would be nice to live in Tampa if this war must go on."

He bent over his dinner plate, fork and knife in hand, but then paused for a spell and looked up at Agnes. "I will be so glad when we can look forward to those little brats of our own," he told her.

That was enough to make her blush.

They were seated at the table on such a night, halfway through dinner, when there was a knock on the door.

Visitors never showed up at this hour.

RG pushed back his chair, stood and walked off to see who it was, while Agnes waited in the kitchen.

All she could hear when the door opened were whispering voices.

She waited more than a few minutes.

When he didn't come back, she finally went to see what the matter was. Making her way down the hall, she saw the light coming in from the street through the doorway, glowing behind the silhouettes of two uniformed men who loomed on the porch.

One with a hand placed on RG's shoulder.

CHAPTER 19

꙳

The death notice was published in the next issue of the *Watauga Democrat,* April 15, 1943:

"First Lt Joseph W Shipley, son of Mr. and Mrs. W.F. Shipley, and a native Wataugan was killed last Saturday when a medium army bomber which he was piloting from MacDill Field, Fla, crashed into Tampa Bay about four miles offshore Saturday, killing in addition to LT Shipley the four other army officers who were passengers. The army public relations office, which announced the accident, did not give further details."

What was so infuriating to RG was that this had been published in the paper as the official account, but just a few days later, when more information was released, it was revealed in the crash report that Joe hadn't been piloting the plane after all. He'd just been a passenger, the purpose of his presence on that airplane unknown to the family.

The newspaper later published a correction: "Young Mr. Shipley was not piloting the plane at the time of the crash, it is revealed." But the damage had been done.

The second and only other update RG's family ever got from the army public relations office said it had been "a routine flight" just a few miles off the coast. A sunny day, clear skies. No explanation given for what had gone wrong. A routine flight, a supposedly routine malfunction. Somehow the plane had dipped and then spiraled down into Tampa Bay, and Joe was lost under the waves.

The crash had been on Saturday morning. They fished his body out of the bay Monday evening. Nearly three full days bobbing in the water.

The funeral was closed casket.

CHAPTER 20

᚜᚛

T he family hadn't been together in years. It was no good kind of homecoming. Agnes hadn't even met half of them. RG wore his Air Force uniform, Agnes a somber dress, as they rode by train up north, passing into the outskirts of the coal country of Virginia.

The trees along the tracks were already thick with leaves, but here and there whole swaths of the forest had been cut away. In the wasteland, scaffolding and rows of identical shacks had arisen, and people wandered around in the smoggy air like scavengers. It was a miserable sight. Agnes could hardly believe her husband had spent his most formative years living in this stretch of country after his family had lost their farm in North Carolina. RG himself seemed so separate from it. His home was the mountains, and now he barely seemed to register the environment they were passing through, as though it were a ghost he could no longer see.

Her heart broke for him. What a disgrace, it must have seemed, that his baby brother should be laid to rest in this gray dirt, and not the Blue Ridge.

CHAPTER 21

T he church was packed when they arrived. All of Joe's
old friends, teachers, schoolmates and peers from high
school were there.

RG's parents, Ed and Minnie Lee, sat side by side with them at
the front. Agnes knew from what RG had told her that it was the
first time his mother and father had seen each other in at least
two years. The word "divorce" was never used, but RG's mother
had moved out of the log house in Virginia the moment Joe had
left for college, and RG's father was rarely there himself, having
taken on jobs with the federal government that kept him on the
road as much as possible, before he'd moved back to tend to
RG's farm in Watauga.

But as Agnes took her seat beside RG, she could sense Ed and
Minnie Lee were closer than anyone else in the church in that
moment, their grief as parents drawing them back together. Ed
was silent, gripping his wife's hand for the first time in years,
while Minnie Lee wept quietly into a handkerchief.

Later, though, what Agnes would remember most about
the funeral was Joe's widow, Jocelyn, who'd sat like stone all
through the service. When people came up to offer their condo-
lences to her, Jocelyn barely seemed to notice, her vacant eyes
seeing nothing at all.

Agnes wanted to reach out and hold the girl. As far as she
knew, no one else in the church knew Jocelyn was pregnant.

But they all found out about it a few months later, in the worst way, when Jocelyn went into sudden labor and gave birth to a severely premature baby girl who lived a few days and then died too.

Jocelyn buried the little girl in a tiny casket on a hot summer day.

No one heard from her after that. Jocelyn stopped answering letters, phone calls. There were no more exaggerated, enthusiastic stories from her, no more giggles or braggy letters. Only silence. RG's mother tried reaching out countless times. She wrote letters and asked around if folks had heard from Jocelyn, but the girl had run off without warning, not even her family could say where to. It was as if she, Joe, and their baby had never existed at all. As if the waves had washed them away.

But Jocelyn came to haunt Agnes in the months to come, because no matter how hard she tried to put it out of her head, that girl seemed like an omen of everything that could soon happen to her.

Agnes learned she herself was pregnant in the summer of 1944, just as the war was about to reach its final, bloody conclusion.

Just before RG received word he was being shipped out of the country.

CHAPTER 22

✤❧

They were standing in their kitchen when he told her, in the small apartment they shared on an Air Force base in Baltimore, Maryland.

It was autumn now, 1944. The trees that bordered the base were aflame with deep shades of red, burnt orange and dark yellow thick as honey. When Agnes walked down the small roads during her afternoon errands, birds would streak above her head, flying in a V formation across the cool sky, migrating toward warmer weather like bomber squadrons toward Europe.

They hadn't been here long, but Agnes had already begun looking at houses. RG had been assured he would be staying here for a long time, almost certainly until the end of the war. "For the duration, as far as we know," were their exact words. She and RG were expecting the baby in the coming year, and the past few weeks Agnes had been overwhelmed with relief and gratitude that RG was being granted a chance to remain in the United States for good. They talked about pushing their baby in a carriage around the base, spending the rest of the war doing their part here at home.

And then, out of nowhere, this news.

"I'm shipping out," he told her.

Agnes stood by the wall in the dim kitchen light. "Where are they sending you?"

RG could only shake his head. "I don't know."

Everything about the news was so strange. A few hours earlier, his superiors had called him into a back office and said, "You're shipping out." That was it. All he knew was that he'd been hand-selected for what they called a "special mission." Not only did he have no idea where was being sent, he also didn't know what he was being sent to do. And no one else on the base was going.

Only him.

"Why?" Agnes wanted to know.

She felt nauseas again. The feeling had been churning within her more and more frequently. All these past few weeks, her stomach had been unsettled, as if she had known this news would be coming. But it was more than that: a chilly feeling spreading inside her, a cold heaviness that made her stop a few times a day and pause, standing still, feeling something detach and then reattach within her. As if something was about to fall apart for good.

Now the nausea and the uncertainty seemed to swirl together.

RG only shook his head again. "I don't know much," he said. It was somewhere overseas. That's all they would tell him.

In the meanwhile, they'd said he should start packing up his things and say goodbye to his wife.

They had hardly any time to prepare. Agnes called her parents to say she'd be moving back to Virginia. They went to the train station two days later, RG kissing her goodbye in his uniform.

The last she saw of him, he was stepping onto the train, and then the train blew its whistle and began chugging away in the chilly October air, while the cold heaviness spread deeper within her.

Once it had disappeared, Agnes walked back by herself to finish packing up what was left in their apartment.

PART FOUR

AT SEA

CHAPTER 23

t was easy to look in the mailbox and spot which ones were from him. All of RG's letters came in the same standard-issue V-mail or "Victory Mail" envelope, ribboned on the outer edges with red, white, and blue swirls, like a barber shop pole. American flag colors.

The paper the soldiers and sailors wrote on was thin and flimsy, though, so Agnes was always careful as she slid out every one of RG's letters, unfolded the paper and began to read.

He almost always started his letters with "My Darling"
Sometimes "My Sweetie"
"My Dearly Beloved"
"My Everything"

When she had finished reading the letter twice over, she would write a response back, then delicately fold the thin paper and slide it back in the envelope. She then placed it with all the others, stacked in a box in a safe, dim place, away from harm.

While RG was gone on his "special mission" – they still hadn't told him what the purpose of that mission would be – Agnes had moved back to live with her parents in Harrisonburg, Virginia, where they'd recently relocated after leaving McGayhesville. She figured she could use her family's help once the baby came. She'd been feeling worse the further along she was, the cold sickness weighing on her more heavily, but she assumed that was just the adjustment period, all the traveling and getting reacquainted with her new living arrangements. Her due date was in early March. Each day, her stomach grew a little rounder, a little fuller.

Each day, another red, white, and blue envelope waited in the mailbox.

But by the middle of December of 1944, Agnes stopped opening RG's letters. Her mother or her sisters could've brought them to her in the hospital, but with the drugs the doctors had given her for the pain, Agnes hardly knew what was going on most of the time. More often than not, she didn't even know who RG was or remember that she was pregnant.

The doctors shook their heads. They told her family it wasn't up to them anymore.

Her condition rapidly deteriorated as Christmas approached. On the worst days, when Agnes could barely move, she would slur her words and talk about things from her childhood as if she were living them all over again, while her mother and sisters sat at her bedside, telling her *it's okay, it's okay, shh...* Stroking her hand, brushing the hair from her sweat-soaked face.

Each day, after returning home from the hospital, her mother would retrieve RG's latest red, white, and blue letter from the mailbox.

As always, she would carefully stack that day's unread letter with the others in a drawer at the house, a stack that grew a little taller each day.

RG wrote to Agnes almost every day while he was gone on his "special mission."

CHAPTER 24

꘏

At Sea
December 9 — '44

My Darling,

We are sailing along now. Things are going very well. I was a little "that way" with sea sickness for awhile but think I will be OK now. I was never so bad. Some of the fellows were mighty sick for a while.

Hope you and the "cherub" are fine + I had thought we might get some mail next week but we will not get any until we arrive.

There is not so much to do on the ship. I have been working in the ship's library — have a lot of magazines and paper-bound books. The Red Cross gave us a very nice kit with soap, cards, shaving kit, candy, mints, a book and I do not know what else.

Sure would like to have gone to church with you this morning. We had a very nice service onboard.

Are you still having a harsh winter? We have started getting our "sun baths" — incidentally they are the only baths we get.

Did they cut anything out of any of the letters I have written before? I do not think they did — but one or two things they might have.

What did the Dr. tell you when you went to see him the last time? Hope you have not been having any more trouble.

Have you taken any of the progress pictures yet?

Well, I guess I will just have to try to make it until we can be together again.

Take the very best care of you — stay as sweet as you are.

All my love,

Bob

. . . .

At Sea
Thursday — December 14 — '44

My Darling,

Regardless of how far you and I get it will never be so far that I will not be thinking of you every minute I have half a chance.

Have you been taking your walks and getting the proper exercise?

Were you able to find a place to keep the car when you are not using it? — I hope so — have you had any trouble with the battery? — I am afraid it will not make the winter.

It has been quite windy and not so warm on deck today.

This should get there before Christmas but I doubt if any others do — so, since I can not be with you, have the very nicest Christmas possible. I will be there in spirit if not in person.

Hope everything is the best possible — if it is not the merriest we will make up for it next year.

If this is to get censored in time I better sign off for now —

Take the best care of you — do not worry about me.
Yours with all my love,
Bob

. . . .

At Sea
Friday night, December 15

My Darling,
The sea was a little rough Saturday and yesterday and it seemed to get me down again. I was not so sick but the bunk was the most comfortable place I could find. I did not feel too much like eating either — I am about over it all now again and I hope I keep my "sea legs" this time.

Since we could not get any mail for a while, I, of course, reread the letters I have — I read them all again tonight. They are all so sweet, so kind, encouraging and everything that letters should be. But I hope it will not be so long before we can be talking in person again.

There was a very small new moon tonight. It would be so nice to watch it shine on the water with you in my arms. It is the first moon we have seen in so long.

Goodnight, my love,
Bob

. . . .

At Sea
Thursday, Dec 21, '44

My Darling,

I have been feeling better the last few days, but I am sure the sea life is not the life for me.

We crossed the equator recently. It is not so hot but plenty warm enough. My suntan is coming along right well but has a long way to go. I am taking it easy so I do not get burned.

We do not know yet where we will be on Christmas. We may stay in port for awhile or we might continue sailing. I would like to do both — to stay in port to get clean and a little relaxation from the trip — and to continue sailing shortly thereafter because the sooner we get there the sooner I can hear from you. So we will just have to wait and see what happens.

I miss you so very much — and if possible I love you more every day.

Take the very best care of you and the "cherub" — and of course, stay as sweet as you are.

Have you thought of any more names for the baby yet?

Yours with all my love,

Bob

. . . .

In Port, somewhere in Brazil
Christmas Eve — '44

Darling,

I guess right now you are sitting in the warm cozy living

room (with a little fire in the fireplace) listening to a program and taking it easy. I hope you are feeling fine and everything is the very best with you. Did you have any snow??

It is quite warm here but not as much as I expected. In the sun it really is hot. We wear as few clothes as possible. I wish I had brought shorts along.

The Col. just called us down and he is going to take us uptown tonight for dinner. We are very much excited and pleased about it. We have such little chance to get ashore anyway — but this is a special treat, this Christmas present for the gang. It really is nice of them.

The Chaplain took some of us over to a nearby naval base for Church service this morning. It really was a very nice service. They had some special music and a very good sermon.

I have not heard anything about the Christmas dinner on the ship. They may have that on the morrow — sure would like to be eating the super delicious dinner that I know you will have, and the more super it is will depend on how much of it you prepare. Everything you do is so, so perfect.

Some of the boys have been fishing off the side of the ship — yesterday one of the fellows caught a nice fish.

After our dinner tonight perhaps there will be some more things I can tell you but I better get ready for that.

Take the very best care of you and the "cherub"

Yours with all my love,

Bob

. . . .

In Port, somewhere in Brazil
Friday, December 29, 1944

My Darling,

Sorry I did not get around to writing yesterday. I was very busy all day and last night I was a bit too tired. We are beginning to believe there is something to talks they tell about people not having quite as much energy here in the tropics.

Think we will go swimming again this afternoon — it is very good swimming but we can not stay in very long, as we are so often busy.

What did you do about your state income tax? Hope you did not have any trouble with it.

It seems to me the nights are brighter here during full moons than there, but it may be just my imagination. There is certainly a lot more light in the day — the sunglasses are almost a necessity. The nights sure are beautiful and I miss you all the more if that is even possible. It has been so long, yes, very very long, since I left you and almost a decade it seems since I have gotten a letter.

It will be a wonderful late Christmas present just to get a stack of letters from you. I will be so glad to get them and I hope it will be soon. I can hardly wait.

Hope you are fine and dandy these days and everything is OK. Write me soon — yours with all my love,

Bob

. . . .

In Port, somewhere in Brazil
Saturday Night, December 30, '44

My Darling,

Here it is another beautiful night in Brazil and I miss you so very very much. I cannot begin to tell you how much I miss you all the time.

I do not know how much longer we will be here, before we move on to our "mysterious destination." The waiting is very nice but I think we will all be glad to get settled down to work. But the work here will be very different I'm sure.

I know it was so wonderful to be able to come home to you each afternoon and I am sure you have not changed unless you are sweeter and more wonderful but I do not see how that could be.

As usual I had my breakfast about eight this morning. If any of us do not want to get up til noon that is okay too. We went for a nice swim in the ocean this morning and again this afternoon. The water really is wonderful and we have a lot of fun 'under the waves' — but it would be much more fun to be on the sea shore with you.

I am getting a very nice tan. I got just a little red this afternoon but not enough to burn. This sun really is right hot but I have been very careful about staying out too long.

Am listening to the 'Hit Parade' again — wish it could be with you in my arms.

Hope I can be sending you a cable before too long saying that I have received a stack of those wonderful letters and everything is fine.

All my love,

Bob

. . . .

In Port, somewhere in Brazil
Monday — New Years Day, 1945

My Dearly Beloved,

How are things with my Darling and everything in general in the States on this the first day of 1945? I certainly hope you are fine and this turns out to be the best of the years so far.

A lot of things can happen in 365 days and I hope the events that affect your life will all be for the best. Since we have to start it so far apart I hope we can be together again for the end and long before. It seems like almost a year since I left you now.

And not to have heard from you so long does not help any.

I better see if I can get this censored so it can be on its way to the sweetest and most wonderful little wife in all the world. I love you so very much.

Happy New Year —

All my love,

Bob

. . . .

Ascension Island
January 3 — '45

My Darling,

As you see at last we are here. Our mysterious destination.

We arrived this morning. I never thought I would be very glad to get to a place so far from home but knowing that I was coming and the [redacted] days in route made me and the others very glad to get here and safely and sound at that.

Of course the biggest attraction here by far was those letters from my little Darling.

I can not tell you how glad I was to get them but I am so very very sorry that you have had so much trouble. I sure hope it has all improved by this time.

Another very bad part is the fact that the last letter I have from you was mailed Dec 13. I had letters from Mama mailed Dec 22 and 26 and some of the fellows had several mailed as late as Dec 28. I will have them to look forward to tomorrow or whenever they get here unless they were lost but I am so very anxious to know how you are after all the trouble you have had.

I should have gotten one or two more letters before I left by ship but I am afraid I would have been much more unhappy than I was, knowing you were having so much trouble and now not hearing from you for such a terribly long time.

Had letters from Virginia, Anna Mae, Pa, Clement, Kate and Josephine.

I can not understand why I do not have any more of your letters. I think there is a possibility they have them here at the Post Office mixed in with some other mail? Surely I will get them soon.

I am so very very sorry I did not have to chance to take better care of my Darling before I left so quickly in Baltimore. Then for me to learn only now that you did not to tell me in Baltimore that you were feeling as badly as you were – if I can get a report to the effect that you are feeling much better now and are feeling good I will feel a lot better myself.

Am glad the Dr. gave you some little good news amid all the bad reports. Sure hope the 'cherub' is a strong vigorous little one and his mother has as easy a delivery as possible when the time comes in the next few months.

Ordinarily they say mail gets to or from the states in 5 to 7 days and sometimes 4. All mail (first class) comes by air from Miami anyway, so with all the bad flying weather the regular mail may get here much quicker. With all the snow storms you had in December that may be one reason why I have not received more of your mail.

There is so much to say about you – the sweetest and best wife in the world – that I hesitate to say anything about myself or the island.

They had told us all the way down what an awful place this was but we are finding it much better than we expected. The days get rather warm but they say we need one or two blankets every night and that sure is good news for me

We will live in tents with wood floors. They have very little rain here. There is certainly very little vegetation in the Island except on a farm up on 'Green Mountain.' We will likely go up there soon on a visit. Our secret 'project' is certainly meeting with great approval from those stationed here. I will tell you more about it later assuming that's OK to reveal.

Looks like they have excellent recreation facilities. Most types of athletics, including golf, much to my astonishment. I had not expected to find one here, of all places. I do not know where they play but I will try to find out as soon as possible.

Hope you are back up to par (eh!) and feeling even better by this time. I miss you so very much.

All my love,

Bob

. . . .

Ascension Island
Sunday — Jan 7 — '45

My Darling,
No more letters yet from the one I love so very very much.
I am still at a loss to know what could have happened to
them. After all this delay I am beginning to think that you
may be very sick. I sure hope I am wrong and that you are
fine now.

Hope the mail is and has been getting thru to you and you
are fine.

All my love,
Bob

. . . .

Ascension Island
Monday — January 8 — '45

My Darling,
I tried starting this letter early this morning and now it is
night.

We went off on two or three expeditions and this is my
first chance to continue — even though we actually accom-
plished very little today.

No mail again today.

If it does not get here soon it will have been a month since
I have heard from my Darling. But it seems like a year or

longer.

Sure hope you are fine.

All my love,

Bob

. . . .

Ascension Island
Tuesday — Jan 9 — '45

My Darling,

Again no mail. I can not understand what can be the delay.

In a letter my sister said she talked with all the folks and your folks included the day before Christmas but she did not say a word about how you were. Mama said she had heard from you too but she did not say anything about how you were either. So I hope by them not saying you had not been so well or something means that you really are fine and everything is going good.

I am so anxious to know that you are fine. You have had such an awful lot of trouble.

I love you so very much.

Please be OK.

All my love,

Bob

CHAPTER 25

A ll day long Agnes lay in bed and looked out the window, staring at the paved driveway outside the hospital building. She kept looking at that driveway, focusing on it as best she could. It was about all she could manage to do.

The days had blurred together. She was sick. She'd never been so sick in all her life. Maybe she'd made a mistake. She'd been lying to RG — no, not lying - but then, she hadn't been all the way truthful either about how sick she'd been, about how miserable and scared she'd been. Why worry him, when there was nothing he could do? Now she looked out the window at the hospital driveway and she kept looking.

It was Christmas. She knew because someone had told her. The hospital hallways were decorated with holly and tinsel and gleaming golden bells: a blurry image of that somewhere in the back of her mind. Or was today the day after Christmas? Or the week after? She could see snow falling outside over the pavement, but it looked so far away, like something out of a dream.

Two babies. Not just one.

The doctors had taken them both.

She kept on looking out the window, feeling gutted, empty. She wasn't sure if she were dying or not. The doctors probably wouldn't tell her if she were. She was not supposed to have given birth for more than two months. It made her feel like a failure. She was so sick it was beyond her comprehension of how truly paralyzed by sickness a person could be. She could feel herself sinking down deeper, but she didn't have the strength to kick herself out.

Where had they gone with her babies?

They had taken them from her.

She wanted to get up, to find them, but she was too weak.

It was Christmas, 1944. She was 27 years old. She remembered now. They said they would send for RG. They would send for her husband. That she remembered too. She remembered telling them. Begging them. The doctors, the nurses. Please, send for him, *please*. And they'd promised they would. RG would receive the news and be on a plane roaring over the ocean to come to her, soon enough. She could sense him getting off the plane now — could see him in her mind, in his uniform, stepping out of the plane's doorway. And by now he would already be in a taxicab, rushing nearer. She would see him soon.

So she kept looking out the window at the hospital driveway, waiting for the moment when she would see the taxi cab pull up, when her husband would step out into the falling snow and come back to her.

CHAPTER 26

Ascension Island
Wednesday — Jan 10

My Everything,

I hardly know where to start.

Three letters from my Darling today.

I cannot begin to tell you how sorry I am about all your illness and about the loss of one of our babies.

But I am so very glad you are out of danger now and 'Agnes Gray' is doing so well.

I wish so much I could have been there.

I had about decided something very bad must have happened since I did not hear from you for so long. I am so very glad you did not have any further complications and I certainly hope and pray you do not have any more. You must have had about the worst possible time. I am so glad you are feeling so much better now and have a good appetite. If I could just hold you and kiss you I think you might understand a little better how much I love you and how much you mean to me.

I am so very sorry I have to be so far away.

The cable has not arrived yet. If the War Department sent one it should have been here by this time and I have been expecting a reply to the one I sent regarding my request to be flown home for an emergency furlough, however briefly, to be by your side.

I am so very glad the little one is getting along so well. I hope she will be able to leave the hospital soon. I am sure she would 'steal my heart away' — her mother certainly did the first time I saw her and especially after I got to know her and she has had it ever since. I love you both so good. You are just the best wife and mother in all the land.

Darling, you know that I just love the name. Agnes Gray — I think it is very sweet.

If the other little girl Carol could have lived it would have been so wonderful, but —

But I am sure the Doctors and Nurses did everything in their power and that is limited. I am so thankful they have taken care of you and the other. I would like so very much to hold you both. It would be so wonderful and such a thrill.

Am sure Agnes Gray was so very sweet with that little thumb in mouth. Three pounds and three ounces — I have never seen or heard of a baby being as small as she is.

I also had a letter from Virginia today. She mentioned about me being a father but did not say much else. I am so very glad your letters arrived with them since yours did not get here sooner. I need not tell you which ones I read first.

It was such a shock. It was good I had a place to sit down.

Tell the Doctors and the Nurses I appreciate so very much the care they have given you and Agnes Gray.

My sisters said they had asked Pa to send you some money. I certainly hope he did (If not write or wire him to send some, however much you need). I will write him to send it and that will take care of it but I am reasonably sure he has sent you some. I know you must need much for the 'specialists' and other expenses for a baby so small and if the government does not pay the Drs. and hospital in full for their services tell them we will.

Most of all I hope you and our 'little alien' get along the very very best. I miss you so dreadfully and love you so very very much.

I wish so much I could at least talk to you on the phone.

Goodnight, my Everything –

Yours with All my love,

Bob...

'Daddy'

PART FIVE

THE ISLAND

CHAPTER 27

✦

While Agnes lay in her hospital bed, RG was soaring over the ocean.

It was January 3, 1945, exactly one week before he learned about Agnes' illness and the loss of one of their babies, and for now he was belted into a seat on an airplane, trying his best not to vomit.

Out the window he could see the endless ocean, the clear blue sky. But just the sight of the water made RG woozy again. He clenched his eyes shut. He'd been a mess for more than a week. Cold sweats, nausea. When he'd mentioned sea sickness in one of his letters to Agnes at the start of their journey at sea in early December, he'd told her, "Some of the fellows were mighty sick," but he'd been sure to say, "I was never so bad."

Well, that wasn't so true.

In fact, he'd been mighty *mighty sick*.

What made it worse was, the journey was supposed to be the easy part. After leaving Agnes in Baltimore, RG had gone on to complete his "overseas training," weeks of crawling under barbed wire, climbing up walls and hunkering down as live rounds of ammunition were fired. With all that training, he'd assumed his "special mission" meant he would be heading out for combat, so the journey by ship was supposed to be a time of rest and relaxation before whatever hardships lay ahead.

But the simple act of existing on that ship was a nightmare. The days at sea were blur of endless motion, the floor rocking and heaving beneath his feet, the chop and drop of the waves, even his dreams rocking unsteadily: a sea-green churn of watery currents rushing into his mind, making it impossible for him to ever slip into the comforting depths of deep dreaming.

Then came the storm. It hit them one night their first week at sea. Walls of water crashed against the ship, all 1,500 men onboard stumbling and falling over one another. There were so many men loaded onto the ship that many couldn't fit below deck, so they had to bunker down as best they could on the deck, gripping pipes and trying not to slip overboard. "A very, very hard storm," RG later called the experience, "and these people on the deck had no shelter and so many of them got so sick and upchucked and you couldn't stand up... I stayed sea sick even after the storm was over."

The higherups took pity on RG and afterwards assigned him below deck in the ship's library, his work no more laborious than pulling books off the shelf, but he spent most of his time lying on a cot in the back corner, dry heaving over a metal bowl.

Eventually they'd stopped at port in Brazil. They were to remain there for about a week or so, until making the voyage by ship halfway across the Atlantic Ocean. An island was waiting for them. Their "mysterious destination." That was all they knew. Why they were all going to that island was unclear. Their mission remained a mystery. What awaited them on the island was equally vague.

But RG was so busy worrying about dying of pure seasickness on the ship, any hard land sounded more than fine by him.

His pain and nausea and vertigo had been so bad that even days after they'd been at port in Brazil, he still wasn't back to normal. Sweating, shaking. Unable to hold down food or water.

Which is why, after a medical examination, it was decided that he wouldn't be able to finish the journey by ship.

But that didn't mean RG was off the hook.

Instead, they put him on a plane early and simply flew him off the continent toward a little speck of rock in the dead center of the Atlantic Ocean.

To a place called Ascension Island.

CHAPTER 28

﹡﹡

S o he was flying.

The plane roared over the water as the small dot that was the island gradually appeared out the window, nothing more than a tiny blotch over the flat blue of the ocean. It could've just been a smudge on the glass, but it amounted to the first hard land RG had seen all flight, the first of anything other than waves, water, the endless horizon.

His journey by plane meant he would arrive days before the others, who would set off by ship sometime later that week, but RG didn't exactly feel lucky about the arrangement. The plane was bumpy and loud and shook so aggressively that it felt as though it would dismantle into pieces and rain down into the ocean. Nausea churned in his gut as they skidded across air pockets. Their descent happened in sudden drops that felt more abrupt the lower they sank against the crashing tropical wind, and RG braced himself as they prepared to land.

If they were able to land, that is.

Before they'd taken off, the pilot had given him a fair warning about the dangers of the flight, but he'd concluded by saying RG shouldn't worry too much about them crashing and dying. "Just look on the bright side," the pilot said. "If we don't hit Ascension, your wife gets a pension!"

But they'd hit it alright – or at least found it.

As they sunk dangerously low over the island, wind whirring around the metal body of the plane, RG could now spot the runway through the window, a thin sliver of black pavement over the jagged rock of the island. The island was a blur of hazy physicality. Carved upon it, the runway didn't look like much. But according to the pilot, that tiny road had been a downright feat of engineering – not to mention a near miracle for the war effort. Thanks to the runway, planes like the one in which RG was now seated could simply soar right over the ocean, above the threat of German U-boat attacks, then land safely on Ascension Island to refuel, before flying onward to Africa. With American and British planes stationed here, they could also do circling routes over the waters of the South Atlantic, shooting down at German U-boats lurking beneath the waves.

All good news for the war effort, but what concerned RG most of all at this particular moment were not German predators lurking in the waters.

No, he was mostly worried about the birds.

He could see them as the plane was nearing the runway: flocks of black and white birds rolling in from the ocean like fog. The runway stretched across an airfield called Wideawake Field, which got its name because of all those loud yapping sea birds. Sooty terns, was their formal name, but RG had learned most people on the island just called them "wideawake birds" because if you think you'll get any sleep with all them squawking and wailing nonstop, well, good luck.

For anyone trying to land on the island, however, the birds were more than annoying — they were dangerous. Their flappy bodies, when met with the velocity of an incoming airplane, were like launched projectiles: they could crash into windows, explode engines, jam into propellers. And because this spot on the island was the only feasible place for an airfield, the planes were at the mercy of the birds who called it home. The guys on the island had even tried shipping in boatloads of cats to hunt down the birds, but the moment the cats were set loose, flocks of larger "booby" birds had swept in like bomber planes and had literally lifted the animals up in the sky, their talons gripped onto the cats' wriggling bodies as they plucked them to death in the clouds, then dropping the scraps of their carcasses down for their feathered Wideawake friends to feast.

Before RG had gotten on the plane, one guy had said, "The cats themselves were devoured."

Even with his rugged background as a farmer, RG still had to admit the image of cats being torn apart by wild birds was just a bit unnerving.

The problem was apparently so severe that during the height

The birds were a constant danger to the airplanes landing on the island.

of the birds' breeding season, the runway had to be shut down because there were just so many of them. The risk was too much: the end of the runway was a jumble of sharp volcanic rock that would shear a plane in two if it overshot. Just before RG flew in, three planes had crashed in the span of a month, fireball explosions that scattered debris and flung bodies off into the ocean.

So with all these ominous warnings on his mind, and still queasy from sea sickness, and about to land on a remote island with no clue as to why he was here and no assurance that he would land safely, RG closed his eyes and let whatever would happen, happen.

His gut left his body as they descended.

Air whistled all around the body of the plane.

The wheels hit pavement.

Upon touching down, the plane lifted once more, wobbled in the air, touched down again, lurched and heaved and then, with a violent deceleration, eased at last to end of the runway.

They'd made it.

With other bleary-eyed travelers among him, RG stepped off the plane and into the groggy glare of the sun. The topical air was hot and salty. He was blinded momentarily. The first clear thing he saw were huge waves crashing on the beach over the dunes. Birds covered the salty rocks around him like dirty snowfall, their white and black feathers ruffling in the ocean breeze. It was so bright, he had to hold a hand over his eyes. Planes gleamed on the runway to the left, their bodies like glass mirrors in the sun, while the plane in which he'd flown taxied to the end of the runway. And over there on the right, were those...
donkeys?

He blinked and the animals blurred into focus.

A whole crowd of bloated, sluggish donkeys was now wandering over the dirt through the hazy mirage beyond the fence. The fat animals nibbled at the rocks, appearing indifferent to all the chaos going on around them: the hot and shiny airplanes,

The runway, a feat of engineering, was still a dangerous and unpredictable landing environment.

the communication cables and equipment, sandbags stacked up high, rainwater reservoirs and water tanks, wire stretched over everything, fencing running up the dirt, buildings and shacks, and boys in uniform running around all over, as the endless ocean horizon imprisoned them on all sides.

"Welcome to the rock," RG heard someone say behind him.

He turned to see a man in uniform approaching him from the haze.

CHAPTER 29

The man in uniform was an officer whose job was to show new arrivals the layout of the island – or "the rock," as he called the place.

Even before the tour began, RG wanted to ask, "What am I doing here?"

He'd expected some kind of explanation when he landed, but the officer couldn't say – or wouldn't say. All he did was walk along through the glare of the sun, chatting away, RG still without the faintest idea what his mission would be on this strange and chaotic rock in the middle of the ocean.

But as far as remote islands go, it wasn't quite as bad as he'd expected.

The officer began their journey upland past the airfield, where rows and rows of Bell P-39 planes were steaming in the sunlight.

Behind them, a Baltimore Martin-187 kicked up dust as it landed on the runway.

Just off the airfield, men were loading up trucks with boxes of ammunition.

They had so much ammo, they kept it stacked out in the open in what they called the "ammunition dump," which was right in front of the "parking area," where planes sat at random spots, wherever the pilots had left them, their fuselages roasting in the sunshine, scattered like beached whales.

As for the planes that needed patching up, they kept those under camouflaged hangars, the roof layered with material to blend in with the topography of the island.

Inside the hangar, men were dissecting an old plane, conduct-ing an autopsy, looking for what went wrong, the same the way RG had once conducted post-mortems on diseased pigs back on the farm.

The nesting grounds of the sooty terns were just up ahead. On their way, RG was warned the birds were overwhelming.

Like walking through a snowstorm of wings and feathers.

The troops marching in review farther inland were far more organized, their uniforms crisp and clean, their weapons glinting.

But the men using shallow wash basins to wipe the grime off their faces looked worn out, thrown together and weather-beaten, like the living accommodations all around them. It was a barren island, RG was told, and water was scarce.

Making their way up the ashen slope, RG noticed the beautiful-ly strange sound of voices rising in a crescendo over the shush of the ocean waves and the breeze.

It was singing, he realized, a whole choir of voices.

He spotted them kneeling before barriers made of sandbags atop which a crucifix had been rigged. They called this place "the grotto." It was the island's Roman Catholic chapel, or the best they could do given the circumstances.

Their singing interrupted by the roar of Douglas C-47's streaking across the sky.

The more they walked, the more RG saw how much the Americans had made themselves at home here on "the rock."

There was a horseshoe pit, tables for playing cards, a chow hall, an outdoor theatre where movies were shown nightly, courts for basketball and sand volleyball.

Even baseball, which was played over one of the rare flat plots of land.

Here the officer paused to tell RG this was actually the second baseball diamond on the island. The first baseball diamond had been situated on a large plot of flat ground at the base of a hill of ash, closer to the tents. But now that original spot was empty. The commander of the Air Force, General H.H. "Hap" Arnold, had personally put a stop to baseball games there – or so it seemed to the guys on the island.

All they knew was that Arnold had flown in some months earlier and had taken a tour with the some of the top men here. Everyone was astounded that the four-star general and founding father of the US Air Force was walking among them. His entourage called him "The Chief," and they followed him as he observed the airfield, the beaches, the tents, the rustic accommodations.

But the strangest thing, the officer said, was that after Arnold got a look at that baseball diamond, the boys were told to move their games elsewhere. The plot of land was being put to use for something important, they were told, although in the months since, it still remained empty.

As for why one of the most powerful men in the world should seem to care about some dusty baseball diamond, none could say.

Outside, the island was loud and bright and windy, but there were quieter places too.

Inside one building, a library for reading or a game of checkers, model airplanes dangling from the ceiling.

And there were also even louder places indoors, like the bar at the "Rotation Inn," where the servers dressed like soda fountain jerks and the men bellied up to the counter under the low ceilings.

There were eerie places, too. The salvage dump where old wings of planes, ripped off, lay like flotsam on the dust. Hollow airplanes tilted shamefully against the rocks. Debris littered everywhere. Used parachutes spread open like gowns over dance floors, spring blossoms over mud, beautifully dirty, elegantly unfurled.

Or the frail lonely tree beside the enlisted men's barracks. It was the only tree on base that had managed to survive so long in the rocks, the cruel wind, the pecking of the birds. An orphan, garnering a strange kind of respect from all the men.

And of course, the cemetery where the dead rest, far away from their families. All sad stories. Crashed airplanes, drownings in the rolling waves, unlucky illness. The dead men, the dead boys really, were laid to rest as deeply as was possible. Their friends hacked for hours and hours at the rock to finally reach deep enough. The bodies laid to rest among ash and stones.

But by far the strangest of all sights on the island was way off in the distance, a lush mountain cloaked in fog, jungle and trees visible by the sheer vibrancy of their foliage, so beautiful and impossible it was like a mirage.

RG couldn't take his eyes off the mountain. He beheld it with a quiet reverence, remembering the mountains of his birth. Smaller mountains rose in ripples before it, with the peak quilted in clouds beyond.

"Green Mountain," the officer said, for that was its name, and he told RG of all the aspects of the island, the mountain was usually what most caught the eyes of all new arrivals. The luxuriant peak of the mountain floated far away in the depths of the island's interior. The name, "Green Mountain," made sense. It appeared to be the only place here where vegetation grew, where plants unfurled their branches and foliage sprung forth. Looking at it from ground-level, the mountain seemed to hover over everything else, like a different world. Misty, layered with deep shades of green, it was the only source of nourishing color on a dead horizon.

But why that mountain should be so alive while the island was so barren made little sense to RG.

He didn't have much time to dwell on it, because of all the donkeys.

At that very moment, a pack of wild donkeys waddled over and began pushing past them, lazily shaking their hindquarters, hee-hawing at RG and the officer as if the animals owned the place. That was typical, the officer said. Apparently the donkeys, like the wideawake birds, were the real bosses around here.

RG hadn't known what to expect when he'd set off on this "special mission," but it sure wasn't this.

When RG was led to his living quarters, he found a spartan arrangement. Tents over harsh rocks, some electrical wires hung haphazardly from rickety wooden setups. A stepladder was even used to hold up one length of electrical wire, its bottom rungs held down by rocks. The wind raged and tent flaps shuddered.

The officer told RG he'd get used to the noise of the wind, but he'd better make sure not to forget to wear shoes if he stepped out at night, because the igneous rock of the ground was so sharp in spots, he could slit his feet open.

CHAPTER 30

✦✦✦

That night, alone in his tent, he re-read through all the letters from Agnes that had been waiting for him here at the island's small post office. It was snowing in Virginia – or at least it had been a few weeks ago, when Agnes had written these letters. When he'd gotten to the post office that afternoon, he'd been expecting a thick stack of letters from Agnes, but all he'd gotten were a few short ones written in a quick scrawl, not at all how she usually wrote.

Worse, the letters were postmarked weeks ago, from all the way back in early December.

The winter in Virginia was – or had been – turning out to be one of the coldest on record so far, she'd explained in that already long-ago time. Windows were freezing and pipes were bursting. Rumors about a coming coal shortage. Snow piled up. Christmas was still on its way, the trees lit up with lightbulbs, daggers of ice hanging from the gutters.

And here he was, weeks later, wearing short sleeves on a tropical island, listening to the wind and the sound of the surf slapping against the beach in the distance.

He took out a piece of flimsy parchment paper and began writing.

"As you see at last we are here," he scribbled. "Our mysterious destination."

He told her about the officer's tour of the island – the planes on the runway and the planes in the sky, the stockpiled ammunition (as if an attack was coming any day, he wondered), and the birds, the church, the baseball diamond, the library. He told her about the strange sight of "Green Mountain," as well as other things he hadn't seen yet, which the officer had mentioned. Apparently there lived a whole town of Brits farther inland, a place they'd named "Georgetown," which consisted of about ten families with wives and small children, who'd been living on the island for years. RG heard the Brits had even built a golf course. "Much to my astonishment," he noted. But they were good gents about letting the Americans play the course whenever they wanted, a token of friendship amongst Allied nations. He told Agnes he'd see if he could play a round sometime in the coming weeks.

All in all, he said, it didn't look like he'd be on the front lines any time soon.

"They had told us all the way down what an awful place this was but I am finding it much better than expected," he wrote. "The days get rather warm but they say we need one or two blankets every night. We will live in tents with wood floors."

He scoured his brain for more to say, but he couldn't think straight.

RG finished his letter to Agnes just as the sky was beginning to darken. He stepped out of his tent and looked at all the other tents around him. Outside, guys were clanging canteens against the rocks, some shirtless with cigarettes dangling from their lips, lumbering over the jagged ground as if they'd been here all their lives. RG glanced up at the expanse of the sky bearing down on him. By now the sun had sunk into the ocean and, as if dissolved in pieces, a pool of sloshing stars was beginning to spread in its place. Some planes rose and disappeared into the darkness, becoming yet more blinking stars in the night sky.

"I miss you so very much," RG wrote when he got back in his tent, squinting by the light of a tiny lantern.

"All my love,

Bob."

CHAPTER 31

✦

O n January 7, 1945, three days before RG learned about Agnes' illness and the loss of one of their babies, the ship upon which he'd originally been scheduled to sail arrived at the shore of the island. Smaller boats chugged out into the water to collect the new arrivals, bringing them back to the beach like taxi cabs.

That night, RG met his tent-mates.

There was Bill Brintinall, who lounged on his cot, reading a book. There was Kurt, who clacked away on a typewriter he'd somehow managed to lug all the way here. And then there was Buckley, who was eating some snacks he'd gotten from the PX right after they'd gone on their own new-arrival tour.

As for RG, he was lying back on his cot and writing a letter to Agnes, his feet warmed by goofy-looking moccasins, the western kind with the frills and tassels. He'd seen one lone pair on the shelf at the PX and couldn't resist. He felt like Davey Crockett or Daniel Boone.

"But I like them right well," he wrote to Agnes.

Their tent was "Tent No. 1." Beside them were two other tents, wherein the other guys who'd been selected for their "special mission" were situated.

Inside "Tent No. 2" were two young guys named Black and Jones, along with a strange older fellow whom RG recognized from their time on the boat as they'd sailed to Brazil. Apparently, the strange man was some kind of professor. The man wore a wide-brimmed safari hat wherever he went, which shadowed his pale face and eager smile. He looked like a character out of a Hollywood movie: the excited academic about to set off on an adventure through the Amazon.

RG's tentmates, Bill and Kurt and Buckley, said they felt plum lucky they hadn't ended up in the same tent as the professor.

"The old man," they called him.

In "Tent No. 3" were three fellows named Ward, Pierson and Mpelkas (pronounced Belkas). They seemed like nice guys from the brief conversations RG had had with them.

But three things left him curious.

The first was that his tentmates had heard a rumor from some other guys on the island about how their tents had been cleared out in a hurry. Up until a week and a half ago, these tents had been occupied by another group of guys. But that group had been told to move elsewhere. Apparently, they'd never been told why. All they knew was that these tents were being "confiscated."

The second curiosity was how isolated they were. "It is away from all the other areas," RG wrote Agnes, so much so that none of the guys in Tents No. 1, No. 2 and No. 3 had undergone the usual quarantine period. "When any new troops are brought in they are kept in quarantine for a period of two weeks' time to see that they do not bring any diseases in with them," he wrote. "We are so isolated from the other areas that it seems to serve as its own quarantine area." As for why they should be put to work so quickly, even to the potential risk of the health of the island, was a mystery.

And the third curiosity was what he learned when he first spoke with all the guys occupying the three tents. He'd asked the usual questions. Where're you from? What's your background? What do you do for work? Do you have a family? And although their hometowns ranged from the Midwest to the East Coast, from the mountains to the plains, and although some had wives and young children and some were bachelors, one factor remained constant between them:

They were all farmers.

Not just farmers but experts, men with degrees and equally impressive reputations for their agricultural knowledge and experience.

RG lay there on his cot that night, his feet warmed by his tasseled moccasins. He felt lucky to be here, lucky not to be out on the front lines, lucky to be resting comfortably on a folding-cot with a group of decent guys in his tent, guys who'd grown up on a farm like him, who all spoke the same agricultural language.

But a single question kept gnawing at him.

Why did the Air Force quietly and urgently send a group of random farmers to an island in the middle of the ocean?

If only he could talk to Agnes about it, he thought – but then, he still hadn't heard from her in weeks.

"No more letters yet from the one I love so very very much," he wrote to her that night. "After all this delay I am beginning to think that you may be very sick. I sure hope I am wrong."

CHAPTER 32

T he tropical sunshine slanted over the group of farmers early the next morning as they stood in a line wearing button-up shirts, their sleeves rolled up and collars pulled open to let the breeze off the ocean cool their necks.

They were standing in what might as well have been a desert. Their tents were just barely visible off in the distance, hazy like the tents of desert travelers in "Arabian Nights." RG half-expected a camel to come clopping quietly toward them.

He wondered if the other guys knew what this place was, this wide-open tract of ashen, rocky land. As someone who'd been on the island close to a week now, he'd visited here before, and he knew from the others on the island what the former use had been of the land on which they were now standing.

This was the old baseball diamond, which had been since vacated.

Now, it was a desert of ash.

They'd been called out here by Lt. Col. John D Torrey, a man they all referred to simply as "the Col." But this morning, the Col. wasn't alone. The strange professor from Tent No. 2, still wearing his wide-brimmed safari hat, stood there as well, and it wasn't long before the Col. stepped aside to let the professor take over the meeting.

Introducing himself, the man explained that he was "Professor Kendrick Blodgett of Purdue University," and that they were all about to make history together.

Judging by the shifty glances of the guys beside him, RG

guessed they'd all heard this elaborate introduction before.

The professor then squatted down low and scooped up a handful of ash right off the ground. Their mission (the professor explained, as he still held onto the ash) was a special one. They had traveled thousands of miles to be here. Had been separated from their families. Had been no doubt confused and curious as to why they were here.

Now, all that would change.

The reason they'd been brought here was simple:

"Vegetables," the professor said.

No one said a word. The wind exhaled around them. Ash dusted their boots. Collars ruffled. The sun kept beating down on them.

Meanwhile, the professor seemed to savor the silence, as if he was under the impression he'd just left them speechless with the sheer drama of his performance.

At last, he said, "We're growing tomatoes, radishes, cucumbers, lettuce and peppers." Then he gestured toward the ground and said they would grow it all right here, right down in the rock beneath their feet. The Air Force had chosen this island because of its isolation and harsh terrain. The goal was to give the men stationed here some relief from diets consisting of nothing but canned food.

"No fresh food can be grown here naturally because of the volcanic rock and lack of rainfall, and there aren't enough refrigerator ships to keep it supplied to the states," the professor said. "And take it from me, because I know – it'll mean a lot to the men here to be able to eat fresh green food."

The men were only more confused now, but the professor continued, undaunted.

As for how they would be able to grow fresh vegetables here, the professor had one word: "Hydroponics."

He seemed to be waiting for some flash of recognition, a collective "Ah!" But the guys just stood there, silent as ever.

The Col. asked if the professor could elaborate.

"Certainly," the professor said. "Hydroponics is the science of growing things in water which has been chemically enriched."

He described it as an ingenious method of growing plants without the use of soil. Instead of letting plants stretch out in the soft nutritional earth, hydroponic plants are grown in inert materials, such as sand, sawdust, or in their case (the professor let the handful of ash finally spill through his fingers) "lava cinder."

"We add to the water those substances which the lava cinder lacks – nitrogen, phosphorous, potassium, calcium and magnesium, in this case," the professor said.

Technically speaking, this was not a new practice. It had been scientifically improved in laboratories on small scales over the last few decades. Ancient Babylonian civilizations had even used similar methods to create spectacles of hanging gardens and floating rafts on which flowers perpetually bloomed, wonders of their era. There had been modern implementations as well – on Wake Island and an equally barren Ponape Island in the western Pacific, for example, and amateur hydroponics gardens had popped up in California under the tutelage of a professor by the name of William F. Gericke of the University of California.

But here on this island, they would be constructing the first ever military-scale modern hydroponics farm in the world.

The professor told the men that in just a few months, this entire field would be lush with vegetables and plant life. They would start by carving growing beds right out of the ground on which they were now standing.

"The beds are asphalt troughs about three feet wide," Blodgett said, as he unfolded pieces of paper from his pocket, reading through the plans. "We fill the trough with volcanic ash and plant our seeds in it. Then, periodically, we run the treated water through the trough, reclaiming it for further use as it runs out. We use distilled sea water," he added, just in case they wondered from where this "treated water" would be sourced.

The guys asked how large the operation would be, and the

professor looked around, taking in the full scope of the dead field around them.

"We have about 80,000 square feet, which is a little more than an acre and a half," he said.

None of the guys knew how to respond. They looked around at the ashen fields, breathing in the bone-dry air, while the wind tossed scraps of debris like tumbleweeds across the barren plains.

CHAPTER 33

B y that evening, word had already spread around the island that a bunch of the smartest farm boys in the country had been shipped in to grow fresh vegetables on the rock. It made RG and the other guys on the hydroponics team wildly popular. Other than fish snagged out of the ocean, no one on Ascension Island had seen fresh food of any kind since the start of the war. It made the thought of plain old vegetables seem downright luxurious. Total strangers were now coming up to them in the chow hall to cheer them on.

"Everybody on the rock knows about it," said a guy from Missouri named Corporal Wayne Burton. "Boy, if it means I can sink my teeth into a fresh tomato, I'm all for it!"

RG wrote to Agnes that night about the enthusiastic response.

"Our 'secret' project is certainly meeting with great approval from those stationed here," he wrote.

But to the guys actually working on the hydroponics team, it all felt so odd.

Their job... well, it was *gardening*.

It didn't make sense. Why all the secrecy in the leadup to their arrival? Why were they rushed here so quickly?

In his letter that night, RG explained his mission to Agnes – as much as he was allowed to tell her. He couldn't go too in-depth, but still he outlined the job ahead, the numerous challenges, and his honest confusion about the whole thing.

He signed each letter the same.

"All my love,
Bob"
He still hadn't heard back from her since well before Christ-mas.

CHAPTER 34

✦

T he day RG got the news that one of their daughters had
died, rain clouds hung over the island.

All morning and afternoon they'd been in the process
of leveling the gradients and moguls of ash on the old baseball
diamond before they got to work creating the hydroponics site.
That was how their grand scientific experiment began: tilling
fields of ash, like doomed characters from a Greek myth.

The professor had already given them the broad strokes of
their project – that is, to build some beds, plant some seeds in
volcanic ash, pump some nutrient solution into the beds, and
abracadabra, grow life – but over the last few days, RG and
the rest of the guys had been holed away in a tent, coming up
with the nitty gritty details for how they would actually make
that happen.

The plan had several steps, none of them guaranteed to work.

First off, they had to clear away the growing site, hence
the group of them all bent over with spades and shovels and
wheelbarrows.

The next step would be to haul two 25,000-gallon tanks up to
the top of a hill close to their worksite – with the use of a truck,
they hoped – and fill those tanks with desalinated ocean water
that'd been enriched with nutrients. The nutrients were chosen
to best emulate those found in arable soil – potassium, phosphorous, nitrogen, calcium and magnesium, broadly speaking
– which would trick the plants into believing they were in fertile

land and not dead, inert material. Once the tanks were filled up and secure at the top of the hill, they would install pipes to run from the tanks and down the hill to the low land, where the guys were now grading the land into terraces. These terraces would serve as their gardens, four in total, where all the vegetables would grow. The terraces were a series of four descending steps, so that the enriched water could flow from the tanks by gravity down into the first section, then drain down to the slightly lower second section, and then on to the third section, then the fourth, each one slightly lower than the one before. The terraces would also have to vary in size: the upper section would be 115 feet wide, while the lowest would be only 85 feet wide, to compensate for the amount of water absorbed by the prior beds.

RG drew a rough sketch of the design of the hydroponics site in a letter to Agnes.

The design of the flow system had also been particularly tricky. It was like an inverse of the Panama Canal locks. Enriched water would flow from the reservoir tanks down the hill and into the first bed, until the bed was filled entirely. Then a valve would be turned, and extraneous water would release down into the next bed. The system would repeat for the third and fourth bed, until the remaining water finally drained back into a sump to be re-used, pumped back up the hill into the reservoir tank, and then flow back again.

The goal was to emulate the water cycle of nature itself: a constant ebb and flow that would sustain life.

Meanwhile, a fresh rainstorm hovered over them all day long as they hacked at the ground in the dry heat, and yet not one precious dropped reached the guys below.

That was one of the cruelest phenomena RG had discovered since his arrival on the island: the floating rain. While there were plenty of tropical showers on the island, the drops would all evaporate well before reaching ground. This created a strange optical illusion for the guys stationed here. They could gaze straight up at a rainstorm just above their heads and yet remain dry, as though an invisible dome were encasing them.

RG wrote to Agnes, "When we first arrived I asked someone about the rainfall and they said there was a lot of rain but very little 'fall' and that you never get wet when it rains. It sounded screwy to me, but that is about the way of it."

It seemed the only place high enough for the rain to reach was up on Green Mountain, way off in the island's interior. There, the clouds scattered showers over the dense trees and shrubbery multiple times a week. That must've been why the mountaintop was so lush. RG and the rest of the guys down low, meanwhile, could only watch from a distance, wondering why they couldn't try growing vegetables up on the mountain instead.

They all sweated until they'd taken off their shirts, feeling the sweat literally bead and pour down their backs. Trying to flatten the ground felt impossible. It was no small job, either. Each terraced garden would have to contain 25 growing beds, and each growing bed would have to be carved out of the volcanic rock three feet wide and 400 feet long. Now that he was having a go at it, RG began to fully appreciate how colossal a task it must've been to buzzcut a field of rocky knives down to a smooth airfield on which a plane could land accurately enough not to explode. They felt like they were making no progress at all.

RG was exhausted by the time he stopped by the post office that evening. By now he'd resigned himself not to expect anything. Each day, there was that dread when he left the post office empty handed. The usual questions lingered: What was wrong? Why wasn't Agnes writing to him? But there was no one to whom he could reach out for help. He'd written to his family asking for news, but they hadn't said anything. When his siblings or his parents wrote to him, they would respond to every question he'd asked in his letters — *how was the weather? how is so-and-so doing? what's the news on the cattle?* — but when it came to Agnes, it was as if they had skimmed right over his urgent questions. They ignored him entirely. His letters back had understandably grown impatient and even a little resentful — *please do tell me what's going on as I am anxious to know* — and then they'd reply with the most chipper letters of their own, asking him if he was getting a tan out there in all that sunshine, never saying a word.

But today —

The post office worker handed him a stack of letters, and right away, RG recognized Agnes' handwriting on the envelopes. He riffled through the stack. Three letters from her in total. Rushing back to his tent, he sat down on the edge of his cot, tore the first letter open and started reading.

Bill, Kurt and Buckley were lounging in the tent around him, talking and laughing.

RG was only a few sentences into the letter when he stood without a word and went back outside.

He walked off in the distance, found a spot on the rocks. He sat there alone, reading each letter.

Then he read them again.

Clouds hung over the island as he sat there, an untouchable storm raging above his head.

CHAPTER 35

A few days later, a communication cable from the Red Cross arrived, informing RG that, on the orders of the War Department, he would be granted an emergency furlough to go home and attend to his gravely ill wife –

But there was one problem.

That cable had been sent just after Christmas.

He also received another cable that told him to ignore the previous cable, explaining that he would, in fact, be staying on the island.

"I finally had a report from the Red Cross on the cable they sent," he wrote to Agnes that night. "It was kinda mixed up but I was able to tell that since everything was fine now my presence was not necessary. It also said the other cable was incorrectly addressed. Something about having forgotten something or other. It just did not read clearly enough to understand it."

The whole thing was so confusing. How was it that both cables arrived on the exact same day, even though one had been postmarked weeks earlier? And what did the cable mean what it said "everything was fine" now?

They'd lost a daughter. RG had read about her entire life – her birth, the days she struggled to stay alive, and the day she died – all in the span of a few short sentences written on flimsy stationary paper.

Carol. That was the name Agnes had given her.

A fighter of a little girl named Carol, born at Christmastime.

He would never get to hold her, never get to see her.

And when it came to their other daughter, Agnes Gray – our "little cherub," Agnes had said, nestled inside a glass incubator – RG was not reassured.

Three pounds, three ounces. That's how much the baby weighed.

He didn't have to be a doctor to know that wasn't normal.

What made it all so much worse was that he knew other people would feel lucky to be in his position — not out fighting on the battlefields, instead doing relatively safe work in the tropical sunshine. But beyond his own troubles, that lingering sense of uncertainty bit at him.

The War Department had said that given the nature of his mission, it was vital he stay to see it through.

What about some ragtag group of farm boys trying to grow vegetables out of ash could be so vital?

And why had the cable sent on Christmas been so delayed in reaching him?

Agnes may have been too sick to respond in those first weeks after her illness, but the doctors and nurses had surely reported her condition. She'd been on the brink of death, after all. It was only by luck that she'd survived. And she still wasn't even out of the hospital. They should have at least alerted him. It made no sense.

That night, RG slid on his comfy tasseled moccasins and lay back on his cot, trying to square it in his head. He was proud to do his patriotic duty and serve his country in whatever capacity the military leadership saw fit, but a part of him still wondered if that informational delay had been on purpose. Even accounting for unforeseen variables like bad weather, confusion in shipping or countless other delays, there was no reason the Red Cross or the War Department couldn't have reached him in time. Had they deliberately kept the news from him to keep him here?

And if so, why?

"Vegetables," the professor had said.
But that couldn't truly be the full extent of it, could it?
Vegetables?
Vegetables?

PART SIX

COLD

CHAPTER 36

✦✦

T he cold came as the town fell silent.

Mid-January was long enough for the warm joy of the holiday season to freeze into a hard, silent thing, and people in Harrisonburg, Virginia, hunkered down. Christmas lights had already been stripped carefully from houses, stowed in boxes. The war effort meant no new light strings would be manufactured for the foreseeable future, so folks had to be careful about cracked bulbs and frayed wires. Years later, an unusual amount of Christmas lights from the war years would be available for vintage Christmas light collectors, for how cautiously they'd all been stored.

But now, in the winter of 1945, homes and storefronts that would've stayed lit all through the harsh cold months sat darkened. So many young men were gone anyway. Their absence was its own presence. Christmas trees, which had become renewed symbols of light and hope in the darkness of war, now lay stiff and brittle under beds of snow on the street. Even the warm exhalations of smoke from chimneys in town were halfway strangled with the apnea of coal shortages, puffs of smoke escaping like choked gasps into the frigid air. Downtown Harrisonburg was in an anxious hibernation, and just down the way, at 198 South Liberty Street, Agnes Shipley was in a kind of hibernation herself.

She couldn't get out of bed. It was on doctors' orders. She'd only just come home from the hospital earlier that week, and if things got worse, she might have to return. So all day and all night she lay in her room, the cool blue light of day filling the curtains at the window, the darkness of night sucking it back out again.

It'd been nearly a month since she'd given birth to the twins. Carol was dead, and Agnes Gray was still at the hospital under steady watch. Agnes hadn't seen her surviving daughter since leaving the hospital herself. Even then, she'd only gotten a glimpse of her through a wall of glass. Now she relied on reports: doctors' and nurses' words that made their way back to her via her mother and sisters, who made daily trips to the hospital to check on the little girl. The baby was still inside a glass incubator, like an alien creature. Agnes herself was still too sick to make it there, although she'd tried. She'd promised her mother she was fine. She'd pushed off the blankets, had ignored the dizziness in her head, but when her mother had seen Agnes' frail body shaking as she'd tried to slide out of the bed, her feet curling and colorless as they touched the floorboards, that was all it took.

She wasn't ready.

They eased her back onto the mattress, pulled the quilts back over her body.

Now, each night, her sisters read RG's letters to her by soft lamplight, while Agnes lay in the bed with her eyes closed under thick covers of blankets and quilts.

"How is the weather there now?" RG wrote in his last letter. "I sure hope it is not so cold and above all that your room stays warm. Since I am not there to keep you warm the furnace just must produce whatever heat is required."

But the furnace was struggling, as were all furnaces along Liberty Street. Some nights, RG's words emerged in steam clouds from the lips of Agnes' sisters, as lamplight pooled and candles crackled in the frigid bedroom air.

Despite her illness and despite the cold, when Agnes managed to get a few words scribbled down in response, or when she instructed her sisters to write a telegram on her behalf, she always told RG she was fine, the baby was fine, and that things were swell.

Inside that icy bedroom on Liberty Street, Agnes and her sisters had developed a routine, a silent choreography. When they were finished with RG's letters, when her sisters had slid them back into their envelopes, when they had all orchestrated responses back to him, and when her sisters had finally stepped back and looked down at her, Agnes knew the same question was coming.

They would ask her if she was ready again.

Agnes would nod in silence.

Then one sister would leave the room and come back in with the milk pump.

It was the same every time. Agnes tried not to look at the cold apparatus of rubber and glass as she lay back, while one of her sisters unbuttoned her shirt.

The touch of the device on her breasts was like ice on skin.

It wasn't her sisters' fault. The baby needed to be fed, and the doctors said it was important to provide a mixture of formula and milk for Agnes Gray to grow strong enough to survive. To do this, to give this of herself up, she was allowing her baby to leave her world of glass.

While Agnes herself would remain in the cold world that was her bedroom.

Agnes was required to pump every two hours or so. With all the preparation it required, followed by the duration of the pumping process, it could take longer than an hour. Half her day was spent like this, while the other half was spent trying to recover.

She could only look off at the wall as her sisters worked, squeezing the rubber suctions to drain the milk into a glass bulb. The pressure and release, pressure and release. The dull, unnatural pain of it.

She felt like a science experiment.

Once all the energy had been drained from her body, her sisters would remove the pump and carry the milk out in its container. Agnes would be left alone in bed as they closed the door, the quilts layered over her like grave dirt, and with the candles blown out and the lamps flipped off, the darkness wrapped around her once more.

CHAPTER 37

꘍

Western Union
YA44
Y CDU41 INTL=CD AMOCOP VIA MACKAY (2 76 31)
EFM MRS ROBERT G SHIPLEY=
298 SOUTH LIBERTY ST HARRISONBURG VIR=
   "PLEASE TELEGRAPH THAT YOU ARE WELL. ALL MY
LOVE.
   ROBERT G SHIPLEY"

· ·

Western Union
**Send the following telegram, subject the terms of
back hereof, which are hereby agreed to (PLEASE
PRINT NAME AND ADDRESS)**
To.: Robert G. Shipley – 34601208
Care of or Apt. No.: Air Quartermaster, Detachment
No. 1
Street and No.: Hydroponics Branch
Place: APO #877 C/O Postmaster, Miami, Florida
   "Am home and feel fine. Baby gaining and doing nicely.
   All our love, Agnes."

CHAPTER 38

A gnes had to wait sometimes a week or longer for RG's letters to arrive, so it was later in the month when she got
his response to her telegram about how she was home
from the hospital.

"That certainly is a most welcome message and I am very very
glad to get it," he wrote. "I certainly hope everything is going
fine with both of you."

Agnes read the letter alone now, having gained enough
strength to at least read by lamplight. RG mentioned the hospital bills, asking if she knew yet how much money she would
need.

"If so and if my father has not sent you some already, just
write him how much you will need," RG said. "He should be
able to send you all that you need, and especially if he has sold
the tobacco and I guess he has by this time. If it was necessary
to mortgage the farm to see that you got the best care possible
it would certainly be done – and not only mortgage but sell if
necessary. You and our little girl are far more important than all
the farms and Herefords in the world."

For now, RG said he'd learned from some officers on the
island that the easiest way to get funds from the government
would be to mail a photostatic copy of Agnes Gray's birth certif-
icate and her medical bills to the Virginia State Health Department as well as the Red Cross, although he wasn't sure how that
process should play out if they needed more funds later.

"If I get the chance today I will go down to the Personnel Office on the island and see about that," he said.

Agnes lay in bed as she read the letter. That was her husband's way of caring, trying his best to orchestrate her comfort from thousands of miles away. She loved him for that, but what she needed most was for him to be here – his familiar hands spreading an extra blanket over her body to keep her cozy; the sense of his weight beside her in the room; the warmth of his voice, telling her everything would be okay.

Struggling to stay warm now as she read RG's letters in the dim light, Agnes could hardly imagine the world he was describing. The tropical sunsets and crashing waves, volcanic rocks and swarms of seabirds. The whole thing was just too bizarre. All those weeks leading up to Christmas, she'd feared her husband's "special mission" would have him sneaking through the dangerous jungles of the Pacific, or jumping out of airplanes, or dodging bullets as he stormed European beaches. And for her then to learn the real purpose of his mission was growing tomatoes and lettuce? Upon first reading that explanation in RG's letters, back when she'd just awakened in the hospital in early January, she'd half-assumed she was still tipsy on medication – but no. "That is the way of it," as RG said, and she supposed him gardening for the rest of the war was better than being in harm's way, even if it defied logic.

"Regardless of how busy we get I will still be thinking of you and wondering how you are all the time," RG wrote in his latest letter. "Heard a newscast today and they said they were having a very heavy snow and temperatures were around 0° to 5°. I fear you are having a lot more snow and cold weather. Wish I could send you some of our nice sunshine. I miss you so very much."

CHAPTER 39

B y the middle of January, a war broke out on Liberty Street.
Agnes could hear the battle rage while she lay in bed. It
went on for hours. Outside her window, echoes of crying
and screaming. Military commands bellowed into the harsh
winter air. She could hear the cannonball sounds of ammunition
pelting soldiers all down the road. The scuffle of boots over pavement, the tumble of bodies landing in frozen grass in front yards.

It was chaos.

For the first time in days, she maneuvered her legs over the
edge of the bed. She felt the pain of the floorboards on her swollen feet, but she managed to keep her balance. She wanted to
get a look at the battle for herself.

The window was so far across the room as she hobbled over.
The curtains so heavy as she pried them apart.

When she gazed out through the window, the street was blue
and brilliant with snow.

Agnes had almost forgotten how beautiful the outside world
could be.

From above, she had a first-hand view of the wonderful battle.
She watched the soldiers run around the street below outside,
dashing in the snow and hiding under fence lines, crouching
behind parked cars and tree trunks, puffs of breath exploding
from their faces like gunpower. There was something almost
staged about it, a performance-like quality. It was like watching
ice skaters weave over a rink, or ballerinas pirouette across a

stage. The soldiers all wore puffy coats and snow trousers, their small bodies thick with scarves and mittens. The imprint of their boots in the snow told the history of this particular battle: lines crossed and recrossed, loops drawn haphazardly in the grass, while big lumps showed where the bodies had fallen.

The neighborhood boys had been at it with these "snow battles," as Agnes later described them, for the past month now, lobbing snowballs at one another for hours, until their mothers finally called them in for dinner. There'd certainly been no shortage of ammunition. Virginia had been hit with 9 inches of snow in late December and a fresh dusting of snowfall had coated the streets almost every morning for more than a month now. By night, the snow would crust hard on the surface, freshly packable for snowballs underneath, and in the lamppost light the streets glowed.

Agnes let the curtains at the window fall closed, turning back to face the bed, but when she saw it – the pillows bunched up, the layers of quilts and blankets – the thought of lying there made her throat tighten.

She couldn't just decay in this room any longer.

She had to fight her way out.

She found her feet were now moving her body toward the bedroom door. For the first time since she'd come home from the hospital, she turned the knob, pushed the door open, and stepped out into the hall. Suddenly, the air tasted different. It was like emerging from a tomb. Light touched the walls gently. A never-ending corridor unfurled before her. She would have to make the journey alone.

Slowly, her legs aching, she made her way down the hall until she'd reached the top of the stairs. She gripped the railing, took it one step at a time. One step at a time. Until she was downstairs again. Downstairs, for the first time in weeks.

Voices were coming from the dining room, floating toward her as if from a dream. She could hear the words lapping over one another. Brighter light bloomed down the hall. Warmth, laughter. She could even smell tonight's dinner. Roasted potatoes, maybe. Or fresh bread right from the oven. Hearty soup. All the smells of the food her mother always made on cold winter nights like this when Agnes was just a girl, all those years ago, back when she could walk without stumbling, back when her body was still her own.

CHAPTER 40

T hat first week after she emerged from her bedroom, all
Agnes did was read letters.

They were piled up downstairs, waiting for her: letters
from family, friends, fellow church members, people from
around town.

She'd kept up to date on RG's letters while she'd been bedrid-
den, but she hadn't realized just how many others lay waiting
for her down in the living room. Everyone who'd heard even
the slightest murmur about her "Christmas ordeal," as it'd become known, had written to her or to her family over the last
few weeks, and the process of reading through each one was
exhausting.

She was still too sick to make it to the hospital, and so despite
her protests, her mother and sisters refused to take her. Agnes
could barely walk, let alone manage a journey across town, especially with the cold and the streets layered in snow. All she
was good for, evidently, was opening envelopes. Unfolding letters. Reading line after line by lamplight. Then hunching over
the table to write a polite response back, thanking folks for their
concern.

The letters were all sent from late December to early January, the worst period of Agnes' life, and as well-meaning as
they were, full of prayers and sympathy, reading through them
forced her to relive through those weeks all over again.

"I am so distressed to hear of Agnes' illness," her friend, Kate, had written in a letter addressed to Agnes' mother on Jan. 1. "It seems such a shame that she had to have this trouble because they wanted so much to have a family. I know Bob will be so hurt too because he is so crazy about her. I can easily imagine that you all did not have a very happy Christmas and I also realize that you must all be very tired now. I do so hope that Agnes has passed the crisis and that she will soon be all right and that the baby will get along fine. I am so anxious about her."

There were plenty of letters from RG's family, including his mother, Minnie Lee, who seemed to be taking the news especially hard, having buried her youngest son Joe and his baby girl so recently.

"I felt so sad all day Xmas day – cry over it every day yet," Minnie Lee wrote. "I know I ought not to but it is so hard to give up the little ones. I feel now more that so much of me is gone... The war has taken such a terrible toll and I do feel it so much – I don't think I have ever felt so depressed as I do now."

Then there were the questions everyone kept asking Agnes, which she had to answer over and over:

"How long will the baby have to stay in her incubator?"

"Have you let Bob know?"

"What color hair or is there any hair?"

"What is the baby's name?"

"Did the Red Cross get a message to Bob?"

"Will it be better for you all to be home due to the shortage of nurses?"

"I hope you can bring the baby home – do you know when?"

"Have the Drs. ever decided what was the cause of your trouble?"

"Have you named the baby? And did you name the one that died?"

Seeing Carol's name go unwritten, replaced with words like "the other baby" or "the one that died" was like losing her all over again.

As snow kept on falling outside the living room window, Agnes did her best to respond to every letter, every question, but there were always more letters waiting at the end of the day when the postman hiked through the snow and slid a fresh batch of envelopes into their mailbox. She still couldn't walk well on her own, so her spot in the chair by window became her only view of the outside world, the letters she unfolded in her hands like dispatches from a foreign land.

That was where Agnes was, one afternoon, when the phone rang in the Davis house, and her mother went over to answer it. Ethel Davis stood nodding and whispering down the hall, her few responses clipped and quiet. Then she hung up the phone and walked over to Agnes, who was still reading by lamplight.

Her mother told her there was news.

A call from the hospital.

CHAPTER 41

"My Darling,

It looks like you are certainly having more than the usual amount of snow and bad weather. I sure hope you are having some warmer weather by this time. Have they told you yet how long Agnes Gray will need to stay in the hospital? Hope you will soon be able to go feed her if you can not bring her home. I hope it will be possible to get some pictures of her somehow while she is so small. But she must look bad or be right on the unattractive side if she favors her Daddy in any way – if she favors her mother then she must be a very beautiful little lady.

Do you know when she can come home?

All my love,

Bob"

CHAPTER 42

A gnes Gray was taken out of her incubator on January 23, 1945, exactly one month after she was prematurely delivered into the world.

Driving through snow and slush in the family car, Agnes' family chauffeured her to the hospital for the first time since she'd been taken home weeks earlier. They helped Agnes walk across the parking lot and in through the front entrance, down the halls and up the stairs, until they'd reached the "preemie room."

They'd made it to the hospital just in time to see the doctor carefully lift the baby girl's frail body out of the glass box in which she'd experienced the first month of her life in the world. It was a small room. Nurses and other doctors stood along the wall, craning their necks to get a look. This was the team of hospital workers who had kept her baby alive the last month. It struck Agnes that in all her baby's life so far, all Agnes Gray had known of human touch and tenderness had come from gloved hands.

After Agnes Gray was safely transferred out of the incubator, wrapped in warm cloth, and placed in a bassinet, the doctor took Agnes aside and told her it wasn't yet time to take the baby home. She still required observation during this serious period – not that they were expecting trouble, he assured her. But with Agnes Gray out of her incubator, the next few days would be critical, and it was important they take things slowly.

Returning to her parents' home that night empty-handed was

yet another loss. Agnes came to dread the darkness that swallowed the light in the windows. Her mother and sisters tried to calm her. They made tea and offered blankets and lit up the fireplace. They changed the sheets and fluffed out pillows. They pried her shoes loose from her swollen feet, rubbed her ankles and calloused heels with minty salve. But there was only so much they could do, and when the house fell silent with sleep, Agnes was alone again.

She lay awake in her bedroom in the dark, her body still aching as it always had since her own brush with death. She couldn't lie on her side or her stomach, only on her back, so she blinked at the ceiling, propped up slightly from the pillows her sisters had slid beneath her.

Outside the wind picked up, snow swirling down the street, the windows creaking in the cold.

It would never end, it seemed.

Sometimes the memories returned to her. The hallucinations from her time in the hospital. The dreams. The nightmares. The strange hands touching and turning her body. The terrible, terrible fear. But now, even in moments like this, when she was alone in her room, Agnes didn't linger over how close she'd come to dying over Christmas. What did it matter? The process seemed boring in retrospect. Morning sickness had turned into crippling nausea, then dehydration, weight loss, confusion. Followed by extreme fatigue, low blood pressure, rapid heart rate, loss of skin elasticity. Decrease in urination, then disassociation, hospitalization. Dreams in the day, feverish hallucinations at night.

Days gone. Nights drowning and barely breathing.

When she'd given birth in a drugged haze, severe bleeding.

Then blinking awake days later, clawing at the bed, at her wounds, asking what happened? What happened? Where was her baby?

More drugs, more dreams.

Feeling the emptiness where they'd taken her – taken *them*.

And yet, at this point, lying in her bed, listening to the wind howl, she simply didn't care anymore.

All she could think about was her one living baby alone in that dark hospital room, how Agnes Gray might be shivering and crying out for her in the cold, and how the baby must now surely be realizing – without words or a specific awareness of it, but somehow knowing all the same, through instinct – that her mother had abandoned her.

PART SEVEN

NIGHT + DAY

CHAPTER 43

"My Darling,

I am so glad you are able to get down to see our little daughter every now and then – It sure is wonderful news that she is gaining and getting along so well.

So they have taken her out of the incubator – that is also very encouraging. I know you are very anxious to get her home but since they are getting along so well with her I think it would be well to leave her until you get strong enough to take the very best care of you and our sweetie. I hope you will not think I am over here some 4,000 miles away trying to tell you how to take care of yourself and our baby – it is just that I love both of you so very very much and I do not want either of you to have any trouble that is possible to prevent. You have certainly had more than your share.

Sounds like you have had more snow than for years and years. I hope it has not been so awful cold.

Did I tell you?

This morning we took our first trip up on 'Green Mountain.' We enjoyed it very much. It is almost impossible to imagine the beautiful green grass, trees, vegetation and the like up there, when it is so desolate and barren down here.

Hope you and our Sweetie are doing the very best.

Goodnight my love,

Bob"

CHAPTER 44

T he trip up the mountain began before sunrise.

Drowsy, the men dressed in a daze, made their cots clean, put on their boots and stepped sleepily out into the cool wash of dawn as the sky spread in gently with the tide. Even the birds on the island were quiet this early, slumbering in the sand like landmines.

None of them knew what to expect. They hadn't been given much warning about this trip up Green Mountain, that strangely vibrant peak in the island's interior.

The night before, RG had been playing bridge in the tent with Bill, Kurt and Buckley, when the Col. had leaned in through the tent flaps, telling them to get some sleep. They would need it, he'd said. Bright and early, they'd be going up to the mountain.

No mission, no details. Just that.

Now in the predawn chill they got in two trucks and drove inland, past the tent settlement of the Americans, past the outdoor movie theatre and the new baseball diamond, and then kept driving way beyond Georgetown where the British families lived with their golf course spread out behind them, until there was – quite suddenly – nothing.

A massive desert of ash, barely even roads.

The part of the island they hadn't seen yet.

It was the morning of January 28, 1945. They'd been on the island nearly a month, long enough to have learned not to ask why they were doing anything. They were just along for the ride.

So many things made little sense to them – their mission, first and foremost, but also each step along the way. The planting of the first tomato seed one week earlier had been especially strange. That morning, the C.O. of the whole island, the English governor and his wife, the Englishman in charge of the British Cable Office, and a few others among the top brass had all come out to the propagation beds for a photo – the professor saddling up beside them as well to get in the shot.

To the hydroponics team, it had to be one of the most ridiculous pictures ever made.

Here were these dignified leaders, wearing their fanciest military regalia, posing with serious expressions on their faces, all while standing in front of a tomato seed. Not a captured city or a sunken U-Boat, but a tiny seed planted in some wet volcanic rock. Had they lost their minds? (Or to use the term the fellas on Ascension had coined for island-induced madness, had they gone "rock happy?") Because that was just the first phase of the planting, the easiest part. The hydroponics team had planned to start by planting the seeds in the propagation beds, where the seeds would hopefully sprout and grow roots. Then they would transfer the seedlings into plant beds, where the seedlings would bud, developing stems and foliage, right up to the point where they would be about to flower. Lastly, they would move the plants into larger growing beds where they would ripen into edible vegetables.

But that was all weeks and weeks away, and if the island's leaders had known just how unlikely this project's success was, the guys figured they probably would've thought twice about that hasty photo. The hydroponics team hadn't even carved out all the propagation beds yet, let alone the plant beds and growing beds. And now that the seeds were planted in the first row of beds, they were up against a ticking clock. If they didn't construct the rest of the beds in time, those seeds would amount to nothing. They felt like chain-gang members building a railroad while the train was already on the tracks.

After those fancy leaders had taken their photo and walked off, the guys had worked all day long, hacking at the charred earth with shovels and spades and pickaxes. Then they'd had to reinforce the beds with an asphalt mixture to make sure the fluids wouldn't leech into the ashen ground. "We have had a right busy day and worked after supper and are going to work a few hours more tonight," RG had written Agnes.

But still they were so far behind.

And now this morning, for reasons unclear, they'd been woken before dawn to take a trip up to the top of a mountain, while so much work remained down below.

CHAPTER 45

T he truck groaned on toward Green Mountain, rattling over loose rocks and divots. As they drove, the sun began tingeing the skyline, so the mountain itself began to blush into view ahead of them. Blue-green and hazy, its sloped contours appeared mirage-like through the windshield of the truck. This sensation was only heightened by the fact that the mountain seemed to stay put the longer they drove, as if they would never reach it. Driving across the wasteland, they felt as if they might as well have been spinning their wheels, and the reality set in that the mountain was far larger than they'd ever realized.

"It really is up there too," RG later wrote to Agnes. "Some 2,800 feet rise in a relatively short distance."

He never missed a day writing to her, but the last letter he'd gotten in return from his wife, in which she'd told him about Agnes Gray being taken out of her incubator, had been postmarked well over a week ago. He knew the weather could hold up the mail, especially with the blizzards passing through North Carolina and Virginia. His mother and sisters had also written about possible coal shortages, and how temperatures dipped below zero degrees all last week.

Still, their letters had made it to the island.

Only Agnes' had failed to arrive.

It was hard not to worry again.

Upon reaching the base of the mountain, the trucks slowed. RG sat up and looked out the windshield. Nobody felt reassured by the roads carved into the slope. It was not a welcoming climb. With a slow acceleration, the trucks began the long winding ascent, their windshields simmering in the sunrise.

"The road was as rugged as any I have seen," RG wrote. "We had to back up on any number of curves."

There were no guard rails, no easy turns. The grooves of the tires of other trucks that had made the same journey before them were their only guide, and they followed these ghost trucks, hoping not to topple off the ledge and become ghosts themselves.

This high up, they could look out the open windows and watch

The view from above as they made the climb.

the rising sun slide silently over the whole of the island. Color spread inside the truck: oranges and yellows, soft purples. They floated upward. They clenched their jaws in the meanwhile.

As they climbed higher, the terrain began to transform around them. Jungle encroached on the roadway, and fog thickened in front of them, a surreal experience after so long in the dry dust. Overhanging passageways of leafy trees made tunnels through which the trucks eased forward, the leaves swiping at the sides and roofs of the trucks like barbecue mops dousing a hog.

At steeper spots, they could look out the windows and see groves of thin trees leaning against the slope. They had never

RG took this photo of the road as they neared the summit of Green Mountain.

seen trees grow like that before. Whenever the groves opened again, RG saw the bare sky, the blurred ocean, and the rounded and triangular domes of rock and dust down at sea level. It looked like an alien planet, populated with ancient pyramids and dust-coated ruins of a civilization long banished from this world.

When they finally reached the summit, color bloomed before them. They stopped the truck in a parking area beside a thick grove of bamboo, clenching the parking brake in place. The moment the truck's doors clunked open, RG took a deep inhale of the fresh fragrant air. What he and the others saw spread out before them was a scene so strange they felt almost dizzy at the sight of it.

"Up on the top of Green Mountain we found buildings (houses, barns, etc), gardens, fences, and all were very typical of an English country side as we have seen in movies," he wrote Agnes.

It was a world in Technicolor, everything bright and delicious and to be savored. The homes wore thatched roofs like festive hats, and the barns were red and quaint, bordered by white picket fences and bountiful gardens, all set up against a misty panorama of jungle, like a painted backdrop in one of the stage musicals Agnes had taken him to in their early days of dating.

RG walked around, disoriented, amazed. It was, he wrote Agnes, "Impossible to imagine." The impossible green of the grass, the impossible dampness wetting his pantlegs, the impossibly soft whirr of insects, as if he and the rest of the guys were encased within a vibrant planetarium on the surface of the moon.

"They had considerable acreage up here too," he wrote, "much more than you would imagine gazing up at it from below."

The harsh reality began to set in. Here was everything the hydroponics team had been striving to create down on the rocks: a perfectly self-sustaining ecosystem.

They'd all been so focused on nutrients, water, and plant life since their arrival on the island, that they couldn't help but marvel at the miraculous combination of natural circumstances that would have allowed for such an ecosystem to thrive up here. But when they talked to the workers on the mountain – the men who made up the longtime residents of this garden village in the sky – they learned natural circumstances had little to do with it.

This ecosystem wasn't created on its own.

It was man-made.

The real story of Green Mountain, which the hydroponics team heard that day, had begun one hundred years earlier, when a 26-year-old British botanist by the name of Joseph Hooker had arrived on the island on the orders of his country's Admiralty. Hooker had known of Ascension's reputation when he landed ashore. His close friend and scientific rival Charles Darwin, who later became the famed father of evolution, had already arrived at the island while sailing around the world conducting research for his seminal work, "On the Origin of the Species." Darwin later said the island was "not smiling with beauty, but staring with naked hideousness." Yet Hooker was undaunted. He thought there might be a way to put the island to some use, so he'd agreed to take on the foolhardy task of bringing some semblance of life to one of the most barren landscapes on planet Earth.

For years Hooker explored the island, researching every divot and dune, every jagged swirl of polished igneous, every mysterious opening in the rocks where shy or malicious creatures dwelled, every pocket of sand where sea turtles deposited their wet, glossy eggs. Hooker came to know the entire island so well that he concluded there was one place, and only one place, that might be able to sustain flora on a large scale:

The cloudy mountain peak in the distance.

The fog hanging in the air over the mountain, Hooker determined, just might be enough to provide sustenance for plant life. He would have to ship in trees, then haul them up the mountain and plant them on the highest peak. If the trees were able to capture enough falling rainwater in their foliage, that might then sustain the soil, and the soil would in turn sustain

RG, far right, and his tentmates on top of Green Mountain.

the trees, a perpetual cycle of life, the ebb and flow of the natural world.

Over the coming years, he continued the slow work of lugging tree after tree up on the mountain, planting each one in precise arrangement to the others, and meticulously irrigating and arranging more plants between the trees so their presence would draw in additional rainwater, hopefully forming an eventual reservoir high up in the clouds.

Now, a full century later, Hooker's dream had flourished more vividly than even he could've possibly imagined.

After hearing that story, RG walked around in a kind of trance. He felt the tree leaves with his fingertips, felt his boots sinking in the grass, smelled the dense pollen in the air as insects swarmed and birds fluttered in the canopy.

If he and the rest of the hydroponics team had been unsure why they had taken this trip up to Green Mountain, at least now they knew this wasn't just a sightseeing excursion.

But then, what was it?

A research opportunity? A form of motivation, to show them what was possible?

Because if so, it was hard not to feel the exact opposite – overwhelmed, demoralized, and even a little depressed.

In the next day or so, they were planning to transplant the first round of tomato seedlings out of the propagation beds, the first step of the vegetative process, and into the plant beds, the second step. It was by far the most precarious stage of their work on the island thus far, and they'd all been working constantly and losing sleep to preserve those frail delicate seedlings. Meanwhile, this whole time there'd been century-old trees and a fully self-sustaining ecosystem thriving atop the mountain, so dense and expansive that they got tired just walking through it all.

It made their own mission seem ever more ludicrous. Comical, even. Why couldn't they just move their seedlings up here? Why did the higherups demand they labor down on the rocks?

If the goal was to grow enough vegetables for the island, the easy answer had been floating up in the clouds all along.

When he later wrote to Agnes about the mountaintop, RG didn't dwell on these concerns. Instead, he mentioned the species of animals that scurried all around: rabbits, donkeys, cats, hedgehogs. Bees pollinated flowers, while tropical birds perched in the higher branches, casually observing the curvature of the horizon as they pruned their feathers with glossy beaks.

"They also had some sheep, which were quite nondescript," RG wrote. "They had a lot of hogs and some very well-bred ones at that – they brought these from South Africa, I learned from the gentleman tending to them."

Much to RG's astonishment, they even had some cattle up here. He spotted them by a fence and at first thought he must have truly gone "rock happy" himself, but there they were, grazing in the pasture. Stopping to appreciate the animals, he felt like a musician who'd stumbled upon a piano in the middle of the jungle.

"The only thing missing were the Herefords," he qualified, "but they did have some Holsteins." And because old habits die hard, he couldn't help but take note of the animals' physical attributes: "Some were right good. Others not so good. I do not know where they got the livestock but they appeared to have been here a long time."

Whole generations of cattle, he realized, had likely been bred and had lived and died up here, floating above the world, not knowing they'd been up in heaven all along.

Somewhere in that time, as RG floated with the others through the mist, he heard it was time to go.

Back to the trucks.

Back down the winding mountain roads.

Back to the ash.

They sat squeezed together in the trucks like hypnotized men through the jolts and rattles down the mountain. The cool mist burned away in the sunshine, and the smell of moss and new growth was replaced by the familiar dry stony air. The truck clawed its way around the curves, going slower. The road eventually leveled off at the base of the mountain and they were back on the barren wasteland. When they glanced back, Green Mountain had once again faded into a fantasy up in the clouds.

CHAPTER 46

T hat night, after coming down from Green Mountain, RG left a trail of footprints in the dry ash as he made his way to the post office, footprints erased by the wind a moment later. He ducked his head as he stepped into the crowded shack that served as the island's only connection to the outside world.

Inside the post office, guys stood around in uniform, all the same, all different, their heads nearly touching the ceiling. By the time RG had made his way to the front, the shack had re-filled itself and a new batch of guys stood behind him, guys who all perked up instinctively when the postman told RG he had a cable from the Red Cross.

RG took the thin piece of paper without a word.

He avoided eye contact with others as he squeezed his way out and emerged into the slanted glare of late-evening sunshine. Red Cross cables always held the potential for horror. Written on index cards, they relayed their messages in a precise and clerical tone, the message always abbreviated – just the bare facts, stripped of backstory or context, tapped out in a staccato shorthand by one of the volunteers back at the Bureau.

When RG opened the cable, the first words he saw made his body go cold:

"Agnes Gray"

It was only when his eyes flicked over to absorb the rest of the message that he was able to breathe again.

CHAPTER 47

✤✤✤

"My Darling,

I had a report from the Red Cross that Agnes Gray was taken home from the hospital the 26th. So you have our little daughter home – I know you are all so very glad to have her where you can look after her. I know she must be the sweetest 'little bundle' ever – how much did she weigh? I hope she gets along the very best and is having the very best care ever... I am sure she will.

Needless to say I am very anxious to know all about her, if she cries, how much, what and how often you feed her and all the many other things I would like to know about her and the most wonderful mother... I love you both so very very much. I hope it will be possible for you to get some pictures of our Darling and her mother real soon.

All my love,

Bob"

CHAPTER 48

The days on the island were hot and brutal, but there was something different about the island at night. It wasn't just the cooling of the air or the relief of darkness. Night was a time when the ethereal qualities of the island revealed themselves. When darkness fell, the chaos of the war seemed to slumber. The tents and equipment, sandbags and communication cables, airplanes and trucks became nothing more than stage props. "Delicate" was not quite the right word, but there was a softness that lingered, the moonlight gently illuminating the beaches, crabs quietly skittish leaving their dotted imprints along the sand. Even the waves seemed to crash less violently against the rocks. The ocean whispered rather than raged. And during these calm and quiet hours, strange creatures emerged from the water.

On the evening of Feb. 1, 1945, RG saw the weeping turtles for the first time.

It happened during one of those all-night endeavors, when hundreds of men on Ascension Island came out to the beach to unload the latest arrival of ships. The ships had appeared at sunset, hulking metal skyscrapers laid horizontally over the water, glowing now in the moonlight way offshore. They were laden with supplies. Smaller boats, drifting away from the larger ones, came ashore like ambassadors, close enough for the men to wade out and unload barrels and crates from the backs. "This was the way of things," as RG later told Agnes, and he described a process that was effective solely because of the manpower used. Every able American had to take part to get the supplies unloaded before morning. None of them would sleep tonight.

It wasn't long before most guys stripped off all their clothes and waded out fully naked. What did they care? It was the middle of the night. As RG watched from the beach, the men looked like sea creatures, slick and glistening silhouettes rising from the ocean, their muscles taut as they heaved supplies onto the sand.

RG's job was to take those barrels and roll them up the beach or carry the crates that bobbed ashore. He'd already slid off his boots and socks and now moved barefoot, his pantlegs rolled up, feeling the cold foam of the tide chill his ankles.

Then he saw the turtles, weeping in the moonlight.

He'd heard about them before, of course. Everyone had. *The turtles who cried in the moonlight while the island slept.* It sounded like something out of a fairy tale, but there they were, right down the beach, like dinosaurs, or like beasts from the Bible. With their armored bodies, the turtles could've been strangely shaped boulders were it not for the slow movement of their flippers, their long necks bending, eyes angled up to the swirls of the Milky Way.

RG happened to have arrived on Ascension Island just as the rare green sea turtles' nesting season began, which would continue until late June. Groups of these turtles came ashore every night now. They were all female turtles who'd swum roughly 1,500 miles from the coast of Brazil to get to the island. As for why they had chosen Ascension Island to lay their eggs or how they'd navigated the journey perfectly each season, none of the scientists on the island were quite sure. The best hypothesis was that the turtles were in tune with the earth's magnetic field, guided by some invisible force.

Whatever had brought them here, RG couldn't help but pause in his barrel-rolling to watch them lumber with their flippers over the sand. The turtles were accustomed to riding swift ocean currents in the weightlessness of water. The burden of gravity upon them must've been unbearable. Their slow ghostly movements made them appear ancient. Some of them *were* ancient, possibly more than 100 years old, according to what RG had heard, and each turtle weighed as much as 400 pounds. One by one, they would emerge from the water to nest, which they did about six times during the nesting season, laying as many as 150 eggs or more a night each, up to 1,000 eggs in total.

Now RG watched the ritual for himself.

The turtles began by digging in the sand with their flippers, pausing every now and then to regain their strength. Once each turtle had carved out a large enough cavity in the sand, she turned to drop her eggs, mucus-coated, into the cool depths she had molded for them.

And as she laid her eggs, she wept.

It was a natural occurrence. The tears flowing from the turtle's eyes were the result of glands excreting salt buildup from her body. Sea turtles don't have efficient kidneys like mammals. They need to weep to expel toxins. For them, weeping is an act of survival. It they do not cry, they die.

Ocean water splashed on RG's face as a strong wave came in, his bare chest soaking now. He grabbed another crate that crashed ashore, glancing off at the turtles as he carried it up the beach.

The turtles didn't seem to notice him or the other guys at all. They stood unmoving on the dunes, gazing off at something unseen, teardrops pouring down their leathery faces.

The beds were carved out of the ground with spades and shovels.

CHAPTER 49

—✣ ✣—

The work in the hydroponics site continued at a steady, if slow, pace. That week, the guys successfully transplanted about 3,000 tomato seedlings out of the propagation beds and into the newly carved-out plant beds, which were the second step in the vegetative cycle. The ebb and flow system they'd constructed to provide sustenance to the plants was working as designed, the nutrient solution flowing smoothly from one terrace of plant beds to another, then draining into the sump and being pumped back up the hill – no leaks, no malfunctions, no errors in the recipe of chemicals – for now, at least.

As some of the guys started to hack away at the ground to build the growing beds, which would be the third and final step in the vegetative cycle, others began diversifying their crops by planting seeds for cucumbers and lettuce in the now-empty propagation beds. Unlike traditional fields, beds of volcanic gravel need not lie fallow. But even with all the juggling of tasks, they were still months away from having anything to show for their efforts.

So they were all confused when they awoke one morning that week to find the Col. was gone.

He'd apparently hopped on a plane the night before and was already back in Washington D.C., where he was giving a report to the higherups.

A report on what? the guys wanted to know.

They had only just gotten started a month ago, and so far, they didn't have a lot to show for it. The bones of their operation were in place, but the flesh – the fruit of a tomato, the cool snap of a cucumber, the crunch of lettuce – was still entirely theoretical. And even if they had somehow managed to pull ripe tomatoes out of the sky by the bushel, what difference would it make to anyone in D.C.?

The guys joked that the Col. must've gone to meet the leader of the Air Force himself, General H.H. Arnold – the man who had once toured the ashen fields of the island, with his entourage who called him "The Chief" – to give a firsthand report. No doubt Gen. Arnold had been waking up every morning and jumping out of bed, anxious for the latest updates on their to-

The beds were reinforced with asphalt to keep the nutrient solution from leeching into the ground.

matoes. The aerial bombing campaign against the Germans was important, yes, but it couldn't possibly measure up against the transfer of tomato seedlings into growing beds. And now that lettuce and cucumbers were being added into the mix? Surely the general was on high alert. Perhaps even Adolf Hitler himself lay awake at night, terrified by the thought of America's future arsenal of vegetables.

They joked about it, but the truth was, they were worried about their gardens. The temperature kept rising, pushing near past 100 degrees Fahrenheit that afternoon. The sun bore down upon them. They weren't reliant on rain or other weather conditions like traditional farmers, but that didn't mean they were altogether immune from its effects.

And if the days kept getting hotter, they would have a problem on their hands.

A view of the terraced gardens in progress. Each bed was three feet wide and 400 feet long.

CHAPTER 50

"My Darling,

I should be getting a letter soon that was written after our little Darling was brought home – I am so anxious to know about her now that you have her – I hope she is getting along the very best and I'm sure she is.

We do not expect much rest for quite some time here on 'the rock.' We have had to work at night recently but do not anticipate much more – I hope, I hope. Most of the time when we work at night it is unloading the boats. We worked 24 hours a day, then.

In the news today, they said another cold wave was really gripping the states – so it looks like you are having some more awful cold weather. I hear where they have closed schools in many cities because of the very acute coal shortage – all amusements and places of entertainment are also closed in a number of places. I sure hope you are able to get plenty of coal and the furnace is heating fine.

I miss you both so very very much.

All my love,

Bob"

CHAPTER 51

◆

While the days were often unbearably hot, nights could be surprisingly cool on the island.

After dinner later that week, RG took a walk along the path away from the tents as the tide eased in. He'd already stopped by the post office right after getting off work – still no letters from Agnes. He assumed she was just busy now that the baby was home; she would write soon enough. Or else, the cold weather and harsh snowfall had held things up. For now, he breathed in the salty breeze that wafted up from the shore. It almost seemed unfair that the air should be this calm and re-freshing, as if the island wanted to make amends for the sun-burn that was now radiating up his neck.

RG was on his way to the island's radio shop. He wanted to make a pit stop there before the guy who ran the place closed it up for the night. He was trying to get his old radio working again. It was one of those cheap portable radios in a white frame, mea-suring 10 inches long, 7 inches wide and 7 inches high (RG had made sure to note the measurements in case that was relevant for parts), which he'd brought with him from home and some-how hadn't managed to ding up too bad on the journey getting here. It was Agnes, as a matter of fact, who had insisted he bring it along with him, so he felt bad having to tell her all these weeks later that he still hadn't been able to get it functioning. Whenev-er he and the guys wanted to hear the latest broadcast, they'd all been forced to cram together in the tent with Professor Blodgett to listen to the old man's personal radio – a prospect that had become less and less appealing.

Having a radio of their own in the tent would go a long way to enliven their evenings.

The radio shop on the island was a small building, a shack really, occupied by a gentleman whom RG had gotten to know casually over the last couple of weeks. Every few days, he would stop in to see if a new shipment of electron tubes had arrived – the last part he needed to get his radio working. Of course, the one part he needed was also the one part that was almost impossible to find.

Ducking his head as he stepped inside the cramped quarters of the radio shack, RG was hoping tonight might be the night, but one look at the shopkeeper's face told him no such luck.

Maybe tomorrow, the shopkeeper said.

RG nodded and thanked him, then turned and walked back out into the cool evening air.

Outside, the birds had fallen silent, resting before the chaos of the day to come, and knowing they were right, RG slowly made his way back to his tent.

CHAPTER 52

B y morning, the Col. had returned from his mysterious trip to Washington, DC. He'd appeared at breakfast as if nothing had happened, as if he'd never left. Eating canned food and drinking coffee as he did every morning. The guys wanted to know what he'd been up to, but they knew not to ask. Besides, there were other more pressing problems.

When they made their way to the hydroponics site, the Col. walked alongside Professor Blodgett as they toured the terraced gardens. Barely sunrise, and already they were unbuttoning their shirts and rolling up their sleeves. The temperature was projected to rise well over 100 degrees Fahrenheit today. In the plant beds, the initial withering symptoms had already shown. The vibrant green of their young tomato plants had begun fading into a dull wilted yellowish green, burning gradually in some invisible flame before their eyes. They hadn't anticipated such oppressive heat, and there was no magical solution to stop it. It wasn't a matter of increasing or adapting the nutrient solution, for that would only drown the plants. The sunlight and the harsh air were just too much for them to withstand. They needed to cool the plants off – and quickly, too.

So the genius young farm boys had come up with an innovative, unprecedented, and thoroughly modern solution:

Shade.

That was it. That was about all they had to explain to the Col. – no fancy misting machines or feats of air-cooling engineering,

The Col. squats as he reviews the carved-out beds.

nothing even close. They didn't have the time nor the resources for that. All they could do was make a shaded covering and hope that would forestall further damage, and then reassess afterwards.

The Col. nodded, and so they got to work.

First, they had to build scaffolding around the hydroponics site so they would have something to which they could attach the shaded covering, so thcy began by digging holes every few meters along the growing beds, like fence post holes. Once one hole had been dug, a guy would come up behind to pound a post deep in the ash, while the first guy went ahead to dig another hole, and the second guy followed to pound in another post. All of them bent over, backs burning. It was like building a picket fence in a sauna at record speed. They went all around, wobbling like ducks. On and on it went, while the sun rose higher, the heat intensifying.

Once the poles were up, they nailed wooden beams sideways into the vertical poles to create a border around the growing beds from all sides. They built it like the frame of a house. One bean was laid horizontally at ground level, then another a few feet higher, and one a few more feet above that, until the horizontal beams rose 12 feet high. The guys started by nailing beams in on their knees, ended it by nailing beams in while balancing on the tops of ladders.

Next, they nailed in cloth shading strips between the beams to create flimsy walls just thick enough to block out the full extent of the sun but with open flaps to let a healthy amount of light and air flow through. The cloth strips were made of marquisette, a fine nylon. It was already well past noon when they got started on the cloth strips, past the point in the day when the sun shone directly from above, so they figured it was okay to leave the ceiling open for now. Better to get the walls up first. At least that would block the slanting sunlight of the afternoon and the next morning.

But they all knew that put them all up against a ticking clock, because if they didn't get the ceiling up before noon tomorrow to block out the sun at its most intense, they might as well have been building a cauldron in which their plants would boil.

They had no idea if the crops could survive another day of direct sunlight. All their work might just burn away.

The outdoor movie theatre offered a view of the war beyond the island.

CHAPTER 53

❧ ❧

O n off nights, when they needed to clear their heads, the guys went to the movies.

Usually these were the nights when they were all so exhausted that the prospect of doing just about anything else – writing letters, playing bridge, doing laundry – seemed impossible. So instead, they dragged themselves to get a glimpse of normalcy glowing in the night sky.

The theatre's screen was outside on a raised wooden platform. The setup wasn't very formal. Guys would sit on flimsy wooden benches or lay back on sloped rocks, some rolling up their sleeves or taking off their shirts in the cool air, others lighting cigarettes, their smoke clouds swirling in the light of the projector, which was situated in the middle of the audience, squeezed between the rows. The guys in the back were seated higher up so they could see over it, while the guys closest to the stage sat lower so as not to block the beam of flickering, smoky light.

After spending all day building the shaded covering around the sides of the hydroponics site, RG and the rest of the guys knew they wouldn't be getting much sleep tonight. They had to be up before dawn to get the ceiling over the hydroponics station up in time. But they didn't feel like being cooped up in the tent – especially since RG still hadn't gotten the part to get the radio working – and so, to take their minds off the work on the hydroponics site, they'd come here.

Outside at the movie theatre that night, the air was fresh with the ocean breeze, but it also carried with it the earthen stench of un-showered men and stale tobacco slowly burning, a hundred cigarette tips glowing like fireflies amidst the audience.

The crashing of the waves behind them made for a soft blanket of sound, comforting now in its familiarity. More cigarettes were stubbed out and fresh ones were slid out of soft packs, hung from cracked lips and ignited with standard US military zippo lighters all around RG – followed by the snap of lighter lids being closed in quick succession – as the newsreel footage came on first before the main show.

Newsreel clips were the only chance the guys got to actually see some of the outside world. "The war news continues to look good on all fronts," RG later wrote to Agnes, after a report that night on the advancing progress in Europe. "The faster it goes and the quicker it is over, the better," he said.

Back home, meanwhile, President Roosevelt had just been sworn in for a fourth term a few weeks earlier, and tonight's newsreel began with the title card:

PRESIDENT ROOSEVELT INAGURATED

"At the White House in Washington, crowds gather for the inauguration of Franklin D Roosevelt as the president of the United States," the newsreel narrator declared in a radio voice bravado. *"Invitations admit 7,000 guests to the White House grounds."*

The flickering footage showed a small crowd shuffling through the snow outside the White House while reporters dashed around them with bulky flashbulb cameras.

"Among the guests are wounded servicemen from nearby military hospitals."

RG saw one wounded young guy being pushed in a wheelchair. Another hobbled with a cane and grinned nervously as he saw the cameras on him. Behind him was a poor guy with only one leg, who somehow maneuvered so skillfully with his crutches through the snow and ice that it looked like he'd been using them his whole life, even though he'd surely still had both of his legs just a few weeks before.

"For the first time, an inauguration is held not at the Capitol Building, but here in the president's own backyard. Now in a grim year of war, the shortest and simplest inaugural on record begins."

It was a brief event by design, according to the newsreel footage. There was no parade, no party. Just a quick speech about America's "test of courage," delivered by Roosevelt to a crowd of military and political leaders and their families, along with the young men who'd been torn to pieces on their behalf.

Seeing those wounded soldiers, RG couldn't help but think of his old high school students.

CHAPTER 54

ᴉ🦉 🦉ᴉ

T hey awoke in darkness the next morning – but then it wasn't even "morning" yet. It was still nighttime, the fringes of the witching hour.

They couldn't even get breakfast. The chow hall hadn't opened. But as they walked through the village of American tents toward the PX, they could hear the soft clanging of pans and a muddled clamor of voices rising from within the chow hall's depths. The early morning kitchen staff was doing the prep work on that day's breakfast. Those half-nocturnal guys who lived in the kitchen like a submarine crew and slept while the sun burned hottest. When RG and the guys walked by, doors opened from the side of the building, and men wearing white hats, white short-sleeved shirts and white pants stepped out into the starlight. The kitchen men ignited cigarettes and inhaled the tobacco smoke quickly. They looked like divers gulping air after coming up from deep underwater. Just as quickly, the cigarettes were summarily extinguished, and the men dove back into the depths of the cafeteria, the light blooming and then dying as the door swung open and shut.

Someone must've pulled some strings for the hydroponics team, because a gift was waiting for them outside the PX this early: a huge bundle of wire.

They carried it back with them to the hydroponics site, and by the light of the moon and stars, they set up ladders and began stretching the wire beam-to-beam across the scaffolding they'd built the day before. Perched 12 feet above the ground on ladders, the guys called out to one another as they tossed the wire from one side of the beam to the other. They tried not to fall while grabbing for the wire as it flailed toward them in the pre-dawn chill. It was so dark they could hardly see five feet in front of them. Some got whipped in the face. Others fell off the ladders and landed like bags of potatoes. Despite a few lucky catches, most of the time they missed it, and the guys would have to spool it back up and try again.

By the time the sun was cresting the ocean, they'd finally gotten the wires stretched over the top of the growing beds. Then came the job of sewing 38-inch cloth strips of marquisette to the wire, creating long strips of shade over the plant beds.

For whatever reason, this morning just so happened to be the windiest it'd been in weeks.

"The shade is 15 feet feed wide and it is quite a lot to handle that and sew with some wind," RG later wrote Agnes. "We are all perched 12 feet up in the air, as we have to sew it into the wires up high above."

He didn't even know if she were receiving his letters anymore, let alone reading them, but that morning, as he was sewing strips of fabric flaps together while balancing on the top of a ladder in the wind, he thought about her a lot. As a master seamstress, Agnes probably would've had some withering critiques to make about his sewing abilities, and he would've given anything to hear her comment on his dubious cross-stich and loops, if only to hear her voice again.

But since they were on their own, the guys kept on sewing as best they could. They pricked their fingers in the half-dark and messed up their stitching. They struggled to get the job done in time, already dehydrated and slow, sweating, tired from standing so high up, their arms moving languidly under the rising sun, repeating the same motions over and over.

By noon, they looked like shipwrecked pirates, woozy and sunburnt as they staggered off to salvage some lunch.

CHAPTER 55

"Another mail and no letter from my Darling. If I could only get a little short note to the effect that my darlings are getting along fine then it would be fine. I know you do not have time to write but just a very short note would help an awful lot.

I hope the weather is much warmer there by this time. I have not heard or seen a weather report recently. The last one told of more large snows in the East. A good warm snow is not so bad but I hope it has not been so cold.

The project has been going a little better but we still have a long way to go.

If you could only hear and see come of the things that go on in this tent as I write – it really is quite a show at times. Bill is over in bed giving Buckley, Kurt, and myself a quiz out of the 'My Little Dictionary' – state flowers, nicknames, populations, etc. I did not know it contained such a variety of information.

We are all a bit 'that way' with exhaustion and may be heatstroke ourselves.

It is now about time for a little shut eye. So for now, good-night, my Darling.

All my love,
Bob."

CHAPTER 56

By the time Valentine's Day arrived, RG had started worrying again.

Still no word from Agnes. Too long now.

"I hope my two little Valentines are the very very best and you are both getting along the best possible," he wrote to her on Valentine's Day evening. He told her how much he would like to be delivering his Valentine greeting in person, how happy he would be when the day finally rolled around that he could see her again. "It has been so long since I left you," he wrote. "That sweet little Agnes Gray has the best Mama in all the land. She has been unfortunate in her early arrival but in selecting you for her mother she is the most fortunate of all."

RG held his pen over the page, pausing a moment, before writing: "I need to know so badly how you are getting along."

He was already exhausted. He'd spent all morning and afternoon of Valentine's Day on "culture duty," which meant he was tasked with maintaining the plants – pruning leaves, keeping out weeds and pests, and otherwise being a steward over their young crops, a job that had gained an added layer of intensity with the heat still rising over 100 degrees Fahrenheit that day.

They'd gotten some shade up in time, but the work didn't stop. The guys always switched roles so no one got too burnt out on one job. There was also "construction duty" for carving and fortifying new beds for the next round of crops, "supervising duty" for managing the work of the team as a whole, and "wheelbarrow operations," which basically meant hauling around materials in wheelbarrows in the hot sun all day long.

Everyone hated wheelbarrow operations.

By sunset, they were all worn down from the long hours and the heat, but no one felt like going to bed early. Something about it being Valentine's Day cast a gloomy pallor over the evening. They all wanted to be back home with their wives and girlfriends, not stuck on this island – certainly not in this sweaty and smelly assemblage inside a tent without even a radio of their own to listen to. They couldn't change their circumstances, but they could at least get out of their tent and get some fresh air. Buckley and Kurt suggested they head out to the rocks to go fishing, and neither RG nor Bill could think of a reason not to.

They left the tent and wandered off toward the cliffside with borrowed reels and rods, the stars pooling overhead.

When they reached the beach, they spotted another group of mother turtles off near the shore. RG had never seen so many up close. Just a few meters away, he could recognize the swirled calligraphy of their shells in the moonlight and the unique spots of black skin on their faces and flippers, patterned like rough continents on a plaster globe. The turtles seemed to glow in the dark, green as seaweed, unearthly and surreal. They were brushing their flippers over the sand as the guys approached, laying their eggs in the darkness. "It was a most interesting sight to see the turtles dig the holes and lay their eggs," RG later wrote. "They dig one large hole about 3 feet deep and then a small one in the large one about 18" deeper and lay their eggs in the little hole and cover them up with sand. They may lay from 100 to several hundred, so they say."

In a few months, those eggs would hatch, and hundreds of baby green sea turtles would climb over the dunes of sand toward the water. But RG knew those hatchlings would face a cruel world. Birds, donkeys, rats, sharp-toothed fish, and other predators awaited them. The odds were grim. Out of every 1,000 baby turtles born on this beach, only one would likely survive into adulthood. For all the effort of the weeping mother turtle he now watched digging her flippers into the sand, she would be lucky if just one of her offspring lived long enough to return to this island one day, to continue the cycle.

Giving the mothers their privacy, the guys kept walking toward the cliffs.

Foamy waves lapped over the sand and the sky sparkled above their heads as they carried their rods and moved up the jumble of sloped rocks. RG wasn't much of a fisherman, but as he slid off his boots and socks, sat down with the others looking out over the dark ocean on the cliff's edge, steadied his rod and cast his line out into the blackness of the water below, he found it relaxed him. He felt the spray of the ocean mist on his bare toes, and the stars were remarkably luminescent. In that moment, he let himself be present.

And when he felt a tug on his line later on, he reacted instinctively. He pulled up hard, and for those few wonderous seconds of exertion and focus, he wasn't worried about Agnes and the baby. His thoughts were only on what was before him. He reeled and kept reeling, and out of the water emerged a dripping rock cod, bright orange like a wedge of sunlight, which flipped and dangled in the ocean mist, its scales glowing in the dark.

The following morning, in a letter to Agnes, RG wrote the closest thing to a poem he would ever write:

"It really was beautiful out there
With the moonlight on the sea
And always I wish you could have been there
Enjoying it with me."

CHAPTER 57

T hen came the hot days, the cruel days, when every new
sunrise brought another enemy upon them.
First it was a swarm of thrips, an insect shaped like okra
that is so small, each could've been a mote of sand. But this
sand sucked the juices from their plants and scraped the leaves,
leaving them twisted, discolored, and scarred: black splotches
like coffee stains, brown smudges as though touched by flame.
When the guys spotted them crocheting their patterns of destruction upon the seedlings, they swatted at them, and a cloud
like dust from an old quilt *whooshed* up into the air, dissipat-
ing in the heat before landing somewhere else, nearly invisible
once descended.

Then came leaf rollers, a munching menace of a caterpillar,
followed by tomato hornworms, creepy green creatures that
glowed in the dark as they devoured leaves at an astonishing
pace.

Lastly, and most deviously, were the mice – or what they had
thought were mice, before the far more sinister culprit revealed
itself. But in the first few days, mice seemed the only answer, for
they had found plant after plant had been devoured at the base,
chewed down as if by gnawing teeth. The guys set up mouse
traps with hunks of cheese all over the hydroponics site, expecting to find them all snapped by dawn, with dozens of limp mice
clenched in their maws – but no.

When they entered the site that morning, all the traps were

empty, the cheese gone.

They scratched their heads over this.

It made sense that one or two especially nimble mice could've snagged the cheese and lived to tell about it, but for all the traps to be empty? They tested the traps to see if they were working properly – they were – then reset them with fresh cheese. Perhaps it had just been a fluke? But the next morning, the same: the cheese gone, the traps undisturbed. Meanwhile, the plants were still being eaten, a nice salad paired with the cheese the guys had offered up. If these really were mice, they had to be just about the most skillful and devious mice in the world.

It took until the end of the week, after days and nights during which the guys had conducted the only form of reconnaissance they would during the war, before they discovered the true culprit was a foe far sneakier than mice:

Giant mole crickets.

One of the guys had found one nibbling at the plants early one morning by chance, a gluttonous holdout who luckily gave away his entire battalion. These mole crickets were ghastly creatures the size of small rats, large enough to fill a man's palm, with big black bulbous heads, pincers and long slithering antenna. They'd been emerging at night and perching themselves on the cheese and devouring it beneath them without even setting off the trap, before bouncing on to feast on the plants.

The guys sprayed the gardens with cricket-killing pesticides and didn't feel one bit bad about all the giant cricket carcasses layering the floor of the hydroponics station, saying "good riddance" as they swept them up.

The bags of dead crickets were so stuffed, it was like carrying sacks of flour.

But even with the invading insects defeated, the problem became keeping new swarms out. Exhausted as they were from sewing the canopy to block out the sun, as cramped and sore as their fingers were, now they had to build a new protective barrier to keep out the pests.

With the netting sewn in, the hydroponics site finally became a functioning greenhouse.

"We formed ourselves a 'sewing circle,' sewing 800 feet of mosquito netting," RG wrote. "We are all perched 12 feet up in the air, as we have to sew it into the wires up high above."

The mosquito netting was the final barrier, a true shield all around. Once they'd tied the netting on all sides of the wooden-beamed compound, over the cloth strips of shade and above as well, weaving it into the wiring on the ceiling – even covering the flaps for air, the netting breathable enough to let the breeze through – the place truly became a functionating greenhouse.

The only remaining enemy was their own foolishness.

Later that week, just when they were certain everything was under control, when the shade was secure, the mosquito netting taut, and the pests kept at bay, all the plants began yellowing, fading, the leaves turning brittle like old newspaper.

It happened so quickly, the guys could literally watch as the plants curled and died before their very eyes, like sped-up movie footage. They walked down the rows – then ran. This was clearly no outside enemy. From the first terrace to the last, all the plants were suffering the same fate. For every single plant to be affected at the same time, it could only mean one thing: toxic poisoning.

It had been their greatest fear from the start.

They must've somehow made a mistake in the nutrient solution. Given how interconnected the system was, if they didn't find the problem and solve it quickly, all their work would die within the hour.

They scrambled, yelling at each other, reviewing the chemicals, and running back and forth, until they found the mistake: someone had added calcium chloride instead of calcium sulphate in the mixture, a mistake as deadly as mixing up powdered arsenic with powdered sugar in a birthday cake.

The poison was already in the gardens. It wasn't a matter of simply shutting off the flow of the solution. They had to flush out the system entirely – that was the only way to save the plants, but they didn't have an automated process for making that happen. So they reacted like a bucket brigade at a fire department, rushing to and from the public water area with sloshing buckets of water and dumping them through the beds to leech out the poison. Back and forth they went, shirtless and dazed, like Loony Tunes fireman, and this went on for hours.

For anyone watching from afar, it would've been no stretch to assume the boys of the hydroponics team had finally lost their minds

CHAPTER 58

"My Darling,
No mail again.

I know you are so very busy and if you ever have time – I guess you are too tired.

If I could only get a little note once in a while it would not be quite so bad but when it goes for days and days and not even a note, how can I help but be worried a bit or more?

Had a letter from Mama and she said you had called her a week ago tonight and you were both fine and the sweetie was continuing to gain. I am glad to get some indirect word that you are OK and that our baby girl is gaining but I would like very much to get some news a little more direct. You have no doubt written me several times and they have just been delayed. I know you are so very busy but I hope you realize how much I love you and how much it means to hear that you and our little girl are alright...

It has been weeks since you wrote the last letter I received.

Mama said they had the coldest weather of the winter last week and the water pipes froze at the farm – I sure hope it wasn't so bad up your way but I fear it must have been.

All my love,
Bob"

CHAPTER 59

+−≈≉⊱≈−+

Another cool night on the island. RG wore long sleeves as he left the tent. The other guys were off at the movie theatre, trying to take their minds off the chaos of the day they'd just ensued. For now, it looked as though the plants would survive. With their buckets of water, they'd successfully leached the chemicals out of the beds and had set up a new batch of nutrient solution. Some of the plants had died, of course, but most were recovering. It was still far too close a call for any of them to rest easy. Better to go to the movies and try not to think about it.

Tonight's showing at the theatre was "Keys of the Kingdom," starring Gregory Peck. RG, though, wasn't in the mood to sit through a full feature film. Besides, he wanted to make another stop by the island's radio shop to see if a batch of new electron tubes had finally arrived. But when he stepped into the shop, it was quickly clear tonight would be like every other night – no new shipment, the shopkeeper telling him to check back in next week.

RG left the shop and walked around the base.

There was still a lot of night left, and he felt restless, but he didn't want to head to the movie theatre, and there was no point in stopping by the post office. He'd already been before dinner – no letter from Agnes, once again.

He walked around for awhile but eventually surrendered and just went back to his tent, where he fiddled some more with the little white radio as he waited for the other guys to come back from the movie. Old newspapers and magazines were scattered around the tent. Some were lying open on his tent-mates cots from where they'd been tossed casually as the guys were heading out. Whenever RG read through those magazines, it was impossible to know if things had changed in the days it had taken for them to arrive – testaments of the world as it had been days or even weeks earlier.

The same was true when it came to news of his family.

RG knew a radio wouldn't solve that problem. Even if he had live broadcasts of the most up-to-date news from around the world, it still wouldn't expedite the delay in the news that truly mattered to him. It wouldn't do anything about Agnes' long silences, or his family's refusal to speak on her behalf. It wouldn't relieve him of the fear, the dread-inducing sensation like a ghost at his back, that something horrible might have happened.

But at least it would give him something else to listen to beside his own thoughts.

He slid on his tasseled moccasins, lying back on his cot, and reached over to the side table for his stationary box. Flipping it open, he looked at the photo of Agnes he'd pinned to the lid, what he saw whenever he wrote a letter. It was his favorite photo of her, "the pride of my snapshot collection," he'd told her. In the photo, Agnes is wearing RG's flight jacket, the sleeves and shoulders looking massive on her tiny frame. She's standing on a hilltop in Watauga with the farm in the background, during the only time they'd gotten back there for a trip since he'd been drafted. The sun shines on her face, her hair radiant. Every time he looked at the photo, RG tried to make the scene come true again, to be there and not here.

Later that night, he took out a piece of stationary paper, picked up a pen and wrote:

"My Darling,

I am sorry I was rather impatient in my letter yesterday about not having heard from you in so long. I know you must be having an awful hard time but I needed so very badly to hear from you. This thing of being so far away and out of touch with my babies is certainly no fun. I miss you so very much. I love you so very very much."

232 Evan Peter Smith

CHAPTER 60

⚜

B
y the time March arrived, the work in the hydroponics station had begun to settle down. Early one morning, RG went to the island's clothing and equipment shop, where he got to work on that day's assignment. His job was to man the foot-operated sewing machine, stitching pieces of burlap together.

"If I keep up with my sewing activities I should be a good house-keeping husband on my return," he later wrote. "I sewed all day Saturday and today. We are covering the propagation beds with burlap to avoid any excess evaporation." It wasn't the most scientific of methods, but they had to get creative when it came to the never-ending fight against the heat. They cut narrow slits in the burlap so the plants could sprout through them, their leaves stretching out in the fresh air but still retaining their bed of moisture below. It was required with weather this brutal. "The temperature rose again above 100 degrees today," he wrote.

Despite the heat, despite the pests and their own mix-ups with the chemical solution, their work over the last few weeks seemed to have done the job.

"The vegetables are growing fine now," RG wrote. "Some tomatoes have even bloomed and some little tomatoes appeared – they are larger than eggs – should have full tomatoes in another 40-50 days."

One afternoon that week, the men of the hydroponics team stepped back and realized there was nothing more to do for

The plants were finally coming along. Professor Blodgett, wearing his safari hat, bends down to inspect the beds.

the day. The tomatoes and other vegetables were protected by the shade with proper ventilation to keep them cool. The liquid solution was flowing smoothly. The burlap was keeping them hydrated. The pests were kept at bay.

Shockingly, they weren't sure what to do.

The day before, the Col. had flown back to the states again for one of his mysterious trips, which meant Professor Blodgett was their de facto leader. Now the old man was giving them orders about how they should spend the rest of their day. It was important to stay focused, the professor told them. They should all get together to study and review the plans for the coming weeks.

Never mind that they'd been up before dawn most days and had worked well after sunset for weeks.

Meanwhile, the professor said he had other things to take care of – no doubt lying around in his tent, the guys assumed, the old man fiddling with his textbooks or writing letters.

They watched him walk off as they tidied up the hydroponics site. In a way, the professor had a point. It was true they should take advantage of the free time. What with how busy the hydroponics team had been, they'd all fallen behind on laundry, replying to letters, cleaning up their tent, doing other chores and catching up on the latest news. A full afternoon off would be just what they needed to get their routines back on track.

So they decided to do the mature and responsible thing.

They went golfing.

CHAPTER 61

꒷꒰ꕤ꒱꒷

E veryone on the island called it "the world's worst golf
course," and it wasn't hard to see why.
        Not that they were expecting lush green fairways or glis-
tening ponds from which gators emerged dripping wet – or
even actual grass, for that matter – but up close, the course was
a nightmare.

They'd borrowed clubs and balls, passed by British Georgetown, and arrived at the start of the course that was run by the
quiet British folks on the island, though even calling it a "golf
course" was pushing it. The first tee was set up on a raised gravel platform that looked out over a rolling terrain of sand, dirt,
rocks and sparse shrubs, the kind of plant life you'd find only in
a desert. A typical golf course might feature hazards and sand
bunkers placed in deliberate spots on each hole, but the course
of Ascension Island was just one giant hazard altogether.

RG lined up his shot, gripping a dented driver in his hands.
Stretching before him was a fairway (if it could even be called
a fairway) and far off in the distance was the green (which was,
no surprise, not green at all; the guys on the island actually
called them "browns," because they were made of crushed lava
smoothed flat with diesel oil). Between the tee and the green
was nothing but black volcanic pits of ash, small caves, rocks
and other ancient debris from the island's geological history.
The same unforgiving terrain the dehydrated castaways on the
island would have seen in their last horrible moments hun-

dreds of years ago, and now here RG was playing golf on it.

He did a few practice swings, the club in his hands looking like it'd seen some horror stories in its day; every bit of it was scratched, scuffed and covered in war wounds. As a mountain boy who'd hardly played a round of golf in his life, he felt bad knowing he was only going to add to this poor club's misery.

Focusing, RG lined up his shot once again, swung hard, and then felt the ball pelt off his club head with an unsatisfying *ping*. He cupped a palm over his eyes in the sun and watched the ball go rolling low over the ground, bouncing along across the fairway, ramping over divots and dunes and rocks, before coming to a stop halfway down the fairway.

All in all, not a bad shot.

Once everyone else had teed off, they trekked forward. In the hazy tropical light, the strange rock formations scattered all over the fairway resembled abstract statues from a modern art museum, a surreal diorama set against a backdrop of blurry black mountains. Blobs of frozen lava. Dead cactus lying sideways like roadkill. Holes with seemingly no bottom.

Not to mention, the countless piles of donkey manure.

They all had to be careful where they walked because the stinky mushy brown stuff was everywhere on the course. So were the donkeys themselves, who strolled around kicking up the dust, looking utterly bored and undaunted by the prospect of guys playing horrible golf around them.

Somehow, RG managed to play pretty well, shooting 44 on 9 holes. Granted, it was basically a Par 3 course, and they made frequent use of mulligans, but still – not too bad for a mountain boy.

"I had a fair score," RG later wrote to Agnes.

If he could've called her on the phone, he would've told her the whole story about the "world's worst golf course," the donkeys roaming around, the strange rock formations, the golf balls lost in the splits and caverns in the rocks, the wobbly shots and lucky putts, the planes roaring overhead as they glided onto the airfield.

But talking on the phone was impossible, and he wasn't even

sure if she were reading his letters anymore.

Even on the golf course, his thoughts were always with her.

And living within this long silence, he was starting to fall apart.

CHAPTER 62

✥ ❦ ✥

That night, with Agnes' glowing photo starring back at him from the lid of his stationary box, RG wrote:

"My Beloved,

I know you have been so very very busy and have been so tired and felt so badly that you have not been able to get half the letters written you would like to – then I come along and am not half as considerate as I should be. I am so sorry about those implications I make about those 'no letter days' – it is just the fact that I get a little on the blue side and I miss them so very very much. Life is none too pleasant on the Rock at best and it is not hard to get a little down at times... the days are so long and lonesome... I guess you have noticed that I even feel better when no mail comes in than I do when we have a mail (and especially for some days) and I do not hear from my Babies. I love you so very very much and miss you so terribly much. I hope you will kinda understand and see how I feel and not be too hard with your ole man. Today was another one of those days with mail but none for me. I know that a lot of the time the letters are delayed in the mail and there is certainly nothing you can do about that. If and when the time comes when you have a little more time and feel like writing I will certainly be very happy for many reasons – first and most of all those reasons, that you feel better.

Take the very best care of you and our little girl.

Goodnight, my Darling,

All my Love,

Bob"

CHAPTER 63

F or as small as it was, there was no shortage of wonders to be found on the island.

Some of the guys on Ascension Island talked about "the rock" as if it were a magical place. It was something RG had heard during his first few days on the island, something he'd kept on hearing ever since.

Usually, it was the guys who'd been on the island the longest who spoke this way, men whose stints on the rock were measured not in months but in years. With their deep tans and sun-bleached hair, they looked transformed – guys who had been living in tents so long that the notion of a house had begun to seem entirely foreign to them; individuals and groups whose natural rhythms had become entwined with the rhythms of the waves on the beach, the sloshing of the ocean foam. These were the guys who regarded the island with a kind of spiritual reverence. *The island giveth, the island taketh.* RG was told to just wait and see. Sooner or later, the island would reveal itself to him.

Of course, most guys just ignored that kind of talk, calling it nothing but "rock happy" delusions, sun-dazed nonsense. The island was like any other island: a natural formation of rock that harbored no secrets nor intentions, no spiritual identity nor concern. Every phenomenon one could experience on Ascension Island – the floating rain, the fantasy of Green Mountain in the distance, or the nocturnal rituals of the rare green sea turtles – had a perfectly rational and natural explanation. To invest any faith in a hunk of dead rock in the middle of the ocean would've not only been idolatry; it would have been foolish.

"That was the way of things," as RG liked to say.

But sometimes, even the most practical of men could find themselves pausing, find themselves wondering.

In late March of 1945, RG and the rest of the Americans on Ascension Island experienced such a moment.

The night had begun with a stroke of personal good fortune: the radio shop had finally gotten a fresh batch of electron tubes in stock, and by chance, RG happened to snag one of the last ones just after getting off work for the day.

Back in the tent, all the guys circled around him as he opened the body of the radio, carefully snapping the electron tube in place. RG fiddled with some wires, checking to make sure everything was in order. Then he snapped the back of the radio in and set it upright.

He turned the knob, adjusting the antenna – but then, nothing.

Dead silence.

The only sound in the tent was their own breathing and the roil of the surf coming far off from the beach.

RG reopened the back of the radio with a soft *crack*. He pressed the tube in tighter, repositioned some wires. And as he was giving the box one more run-through, suddenly a soft fuzz of static began to emerge from the speaker, pressed as it was face-down on the table.

Everyone leaned back.

Carefully, RG set the radio upright. The volume rose un-smothered. It was only static at first, and he waited a few more seconds, before delicately adjusting the antenna. The guys waited in silence around him. With one last adjustment, RG turned the dial, and all at once a faint hum poured from the speaker, like water flowing through a suddenly unclogged pipe.

Music.

They heard violins, gentle as birds coasting in the sky.

And piano notes like rain drops, splattering upon a roof.
Then a voice, warm and close, rising as if from a memory:

Night and day...
You are the one...

And that's when RG froze.

The other guys around him could've been cheering and slapping him on the back for finally getting the radio working. He wouldn't have felt it, wouldn't have heard it.

He couldn't move at all. Could barely breathe. He sat like a statue, trying to wrap his mind around it.

What are the odds? he thought.

Of all the songs in the world, of all the places he could've been, of all the broadcasts and of all the times he could've got the radio working, how could it possibly be this song, *their* song, that first came through the speakers?

The very same song he and Agnes had danced along to countless times in the living room of the brick house on the farm all those years ago:

Only you 'neath the moon
Or under the stars

Now, as Frank Sinatra's voice filled the tent, it seemed to pour around RG like ocean water and lift him up in a Biblical tide, lift him right through the tent's ceiling and high above the American basecamp, above the beach and the airfield, above the radio tower and higher even than Green Mountain with its coiled foliage and damp silence, its misty fields, its glossy birds and sleeping cattle, and then gently placed RG back down in the mountains of his birth, back in the brick house on the farm on a warm summer night all those years ago, when the windows were open, the smell of the fields lathering the air, as moonlight glowed through the curtains.

It's no matter darling
Where you are...

The feel of Agnes' cheek pressed against his chest, her hand in his hand.

I think of you...
Day and night...
Night and day...

And RG would've gladly stayed there in his mind, holding Agnes in his arms again, swaying to the music in a place untouched by war, with a love unburdened by distance, had someone not started screaming outside their tent.

RG shut off the radio.

Then they all froze, waiting for what came next.

CHAPTER 64

S ilence now, as the guys all leaned over the edges of their cots. No one inside the tent said a word. They just waited.

Now the screaming began again.

Louder this time. Urgent. Yelling, voices rising. From the beach, they realized. And below the screaming, they could hear the rustle of men running, the scrape of boots on rocks. Murmurs now from the tents around them. Lanterns shut off, the whisper of bodies rushing through tent flaps.

The island hadn't been attacked by U-boats in more than a year, but it was possible –

RG, Buckley, Kurt and Bill all looked at each other.

Then, without a word, they rushed out into the night air.

The time was exactly 10:12 p.m. RG knew that because he'd glanced at his watch as he ran out with all the others, and he would make sure to remember that detail, to make a note in his mind, because he wanted to have all the facts of this evening correct. He wanted to make sure he didn't miss anything. To explain in the fullest extent that what he'd seen that night, glowing over the ocean, was real. That he'd seen it with his own eyes. They all had.

The guys crested the dunes and came to a stop on the beach, where they beheld the sky glowing and pulsing with light.

"A rainbow," RG later wrote. "A rainbow at night."

Hundreds more were pouring out of their tents, all yelling and screaming now for others to come and look. The colors of the rainbow were tinged blue, but it was as clear as any rainbow RG had ever seen. It floated silkily over the ocean in the black sky like a radiant ghost.

The whole island came out to see it – even the turtles.

Farther down the beach, mother sea turtles were lined up over the sand, their shells gleaming under the dreamy light of the lunar rainbow, their eyes glistening with salty tears.

Once the yelling had quieted down, the only sound was the soft slosh of the waves over the sand. Men didn't even think to light cigarettes. Some took off the hats they'd been wearing, out of reverence. Others prayed. The rainbow glowed as if painted by angels. It didn't seem real. It couldn't possibly be real. RG, like so many others, was totally silent, trying to square what he was seeing with the physical limits of reality.

"Now do not say I must be 'tipsy,'" he later wrote Agnes. "We all saw it and it is certainly very unusual – lit by moonlight, the first time any of us have seen anything like it. I have never heard before of such a thing being possible."

Later that week, when a letter from Agnes finally arrived on the island in response, it was hard not to regard this night on the beach as a turning point – the moment when the rising tide of his life fell back, when the harsh waters of the last few months finally calmed.

RG was not the type to believe in the superstitions some held about the island, but even though he could later search through a textbook to find the rare accounts of rainbows appearing at night throughout history, or consult a meteorologist to learn the exceedingly unusual – *but not impossible* – combination of rainfall, the moon's angle in orbit, and light refraction required to create a lunar rainbow, it still wouldn't change the awe he'd felt as he'd stood there on that beach, all the silent men and sobbing turtles around him, gazing up at those gleaming brush-strokes painted across the night sky.

PART EIGHT

HERE BY THE OWL

CHAPTER 65

✦

Months later, after the war was over, Agnes was shopping in the grocery store in downtown Harrisonburg, Virginia, when she happened to pass by the magazine rack near the store's entrance.

Some things in the grocery store had changed since the fighting in Europe and the Pacific was over – there was more butter now, for instance, and even some sugar too. Shelves that had been empty were now full again. Ration cards were gradually falling by the wayside, and smiles were more common on the faces of the staff in their uniforms and their customers too. But the one truly dynamic portion of this little storefront in the middle of the country was that magazine rack near the front. Amidst check-out counters and bins of vegetables, the magazine rack served as a window into the rest of the world.

Every one of the shoppers in that grocery store was lucky enough to live in a time when advanced technology granted them almost immediate access to the most up-to-date information. They got to grab glimpses of the latest news across the globe, with its potential for bloodshed and horror, as easily as grabbing a loaf of bread off the shelf, slipping them into grocery baskets alongside sticks of butter and cans of beans. They'd all gotten very matter of fact about it.

In early May, magazine covers had run the news that Hitler was dead, his thousand-year regime lying in ruins all around him. The war in Europe ended a few weeks later, when the town was fully in bloom and school was getting ready to let out. That week, the covers of the magazines in the rack showed people dancing in the streets of New York, American GIs posing on the roofs of gutted Nazi palaces, and little kids waving American flags from the backs of pickup trucks in small towns across America.

Outside the grocery store, on the sidewalks of Liberty Street, children skipped by the windows, young mothers pushed babies in strollers, and old folks smiled fully for the first time in years.

Summer arrived, and with it came the arrival of more trains rolling into town, full of young men returning from Europe in their crisp uniforms. It was a surreal thing to see them strolling the streets now, after so many years when the sight of a healthy young man was a rarity. High school girls in their jumpers blushed whenever they saw one coming down the sidewalk. The charming young men tipped their caps and smiled. Other men seemed blinded and wandered aimlessly, blinking in the unfamiliar sunlight of normalcy.

That year's 4th of July celebration was the most festive in decades. President Truman gave a radio message honoring America's "creed of liberty, and the men and women of our armed forces who are carrying this creed with them throughout the world." Agnes and her family celebrated the holiday with a cookout in their backyard. When they went for a walk through the neighborhood later that afternoon, Agnes pushing little Agnes Gray in a stroller, they passed by quiet homes with gold stars in the windows.

CHAPTER 66

C hange had come slowly over the last half year – with the war, with the weather, and with Agnes herself.

Winter had felt like a half-awake nightmare. She'd just about blocked it out: the nights and days sick in bed, nauseas and swollen. The pain in her limbs, the pounding in her head. The disassociation from reality.

She'd thought bringing the baby home from the hospital would be the end of the worst part, but it was only the beginning.

Virginia had been in the grips of an unceasing cold. Liberty Street had been frozen over for weeks, dirty snow piled along the curbs. Nights were especially brutal. Pipes were freezing in homes all over town, and the coal shortage would not let up. The furnace in their own house was barely being used. Agnes had resorted to using hot water bottles wrapped in cloth and placing them around Agnes Gray in her crib to keep her warm at night. Even so, the baby usually cried until morning. When she wasn't crying, Agnes would be down at the stove in the kitchen, boiling more water to refill the water bottles to keep her warm. She didn't have a full night's sleep in weeks.

"I am truly getting concerned about my mind," she told her family.

Soon she couldn't even write RG to tell him about her trouble, because she simply wasn't physically able to do so. In February, her hands and feet began swelling three times their normal size, turning her fingers and toes into plump sausages, unable to bend easily.

Nothing to worry about, said the doctors.

A common side effect, they said.

Should remedy itself soon enough.

Meanwhile, it made gripping a pen and writing a letter all but impossible, and taking care of the baby just as difficult. When changing diapers, Agnes might as well have been wearing oven mitts. Making her way down the stairs at night to refill the warm water bottles was a terribly slow affair; standing by the boiling kettle a painful feat of endurance (she had to pull up a chair and sit as the water boiled); and filling the bottles all but impossible, for she couldn't even grasp the handle of the kettle, couldn't screw the lids back on without help from her mother and sisters. After a few tries at wobbling back upstairs with her swollen feet, the bottles tucked under her arms, she gave up. Agnes let her sisters and her mother resume as the baby's primary caretakers, while she returned to painful hibernation in her bedroom.

Weeks went by.

All through those cold gray days and freezing dark nights, she'd felt as though every bright color from the world had been wrung out as if from a dirty rag, leaving everything limp and useless.

She didn't read any of RG's letters. She barely saw her daughter. Her sisters kept pumping milk from her.

She hardly even noticed the weather changing.

The sound of birdsong in the morning, or the lengthening of the days.

But one morning in March, as the curtains at the window marinated in warm sunlight, Agnes had woken up feeling slightly better than she had the day before. It was hardly noticeable, as though someone had simply removed a few pounds from a hundred-pound bag she'd been forced to carry.

But the next day had been just a little easier, a little lighter, a few more stones removed.

And so too was the day after.

Agnes knew not to put much stock in it. She'd been through cruel swings of good health before, which had lasted just long enough to convince her she was finally improving for good, only to plummet her shortly thereafter into another bout of horrific illness. So, in a strange way, the improvements only increased her anxiety. As she watched her swollen hands and feet begin to deflate back to their normal size, the first thing she did was fold her hands together to pray her spirit wouldn't be broken again.

The temperature continued to rise with the waning days of winter, and mornings now Agnes was able to slide the bed-sheets off her body and step down on the floorboards without any sharp pain shooting up her legs. She could wiggle her toes again, could clench a pen in her hand without effort.

Then spring arrived.

Windows were slid open; a warm and fresh breeze exhaled through the house.

For the first time in months, Agnes wrote her husband a long letter and didn't wince with each pen stroke.

"I have heard tell that you shouldn't live in the past," she told him, "but when I think of all the fun and joys we have had in the past it makes me that much more anxious for the future, when we can be together forever + ever... You are with me wherever I go – 'even tho we're far apart, you are always in my heart.'"

But even as her strength grew, Agnes never managed to feel like herself again.

As good as it was to be moving around, she still felt changed, and despite her best efforts, that old sense of herself never re-turned. Her hands and feet looked different, for one. Parts of her body were scarred, transformed – heavy in some places, fa-tigued and frail in others. At times, she felt like stranger inside her own body. She even wrote to RG, warning him that he might not like the woman she'd become, with her stretched skin and bloated stomach, and how she couldn't fit into old clothes because of her expanded waistline.

"I would not worry about that," RG wrote back. "By the time I have squeezed you so tight for so long, your waist will probably be at an all time minimum!"

He told her it didn't matter what she looked like. He just wanted to see her again.

"You are already perfect in every way," he said.

And Agnes tried her best to believe him.

CHAPTER 67

⭐

A s much as she fretted about the changes in her body, people around town noticed a different kind of change in Agnes.

By the time spring had slid into summer, whenever she went for a walk around the neighborhood, Agnes became the subject of gossip down the street. It was an odd déjà vu feeling that reminded her of those years back in McGayesville as young woman walking to and from college. Since it was early summer, all the windows of the homes along Liberty Street in downtown Harrisonburg had been flung open to the breeze, and anyone who happened to glance out and spot Agnes in her pretty dress, with her healthy baby in the stroller, did a double take. She looked very much like the subject of a Norman Rockwell painting: a beautiful young mother out for a healthy walk in the summer air, wearing a fine new dress, while her plump baby gazed with wonder at the blossoms in the trees, sucking on a pacifier.

All winter, rumors down the street had said Agnes was near death. She was a frail creature, they said, who sulked in the cold darkness, and her daughter was no better off: a skeleton baby with no chance at life. For them both to then bloom so vividly in the sunny light of the window frame in summer was enough to become the topic of dinner table conversations all down the block.

Later that summer, when her husband became famous, that

only increased the gossip about the young Mrs. Shipley.

Agnes, for her part, would've said "famous" wasn't the right word for it, but even she had to admit it was a funny thing to see RG's team and their mission featured so much in the national news, especially when she herself hadn't anticipated it at all.

In early August, she was in the grocery store, passing by the magazine rack, when she happened to spot the cover of the latest issue of "National Geographic," which made her whip back so hard, she almost kinked her neck.

"Greens Grow for GI's on Soilless Ascension," read the headline on the cover of the August edition of the magazine.

Agnes dropped her grocery basket and grabbed the edition off the rack and started flipping through its pages. RG had mentioned off-hand in a letter a few weeks earlier that some reporters from the "National Geographic" had made a pit stop on the island, but in classic RG fashion, he hadn't mentioned anything about a story on the hydroponics team. Yet here were pages and pages of photos – of her husband and other men hunched over beds of vegetables, of hills and mountains of ash, of giant turtles glowing in the sand and blizzards of snow-white birds filling the sky – along with 12 pages of detailed reporting on the mission of the hydroponics team, which the magazine called, "The Army's latest triumph."

"Look at Ascension Island and you appreciate why the growing of green vegetables here makes news," wrote the reporter, W. Robert Moore. "Virtually the whole area is as devoid of vegetation as the dump pit of a furnace."

But thanks to the "the magic of hydroponics," W. Robert Moore was able to witness an abundant harvest, soldiers "enthusiastically piling lettuce leaves between slabs of bread to make a huge fresh sandwich," while others feasted on the bounty of cucumbers, tomatoes, radishes and green peppers.

When speaking of RG and the rest of the team, W. Robert Moore called them "chemists and valve turners, rather than men with shovels and hoes." He described them as mod-

The hydroponics team and some engineers from the island. RG is standing in the top row, third from the left.

ern-day alchemists who had created life from the ashes, using ingenious potions of potassium, phosphorous, nitrogen, calcium and magnesium, all with very little water – and all by designs they'd engineered and constructed on their own, while dealing with on-the-fly challenges, to bring to life the broad strokes of theory, despite no per-ordained blueprint nor detailed strategy. They'd fought off armies of rodents and pests, which would've liked to devour the vegetables for themselves. They'd even called for a shipment of honeybees to be brought by airplane from Brazil in order to pollinate the crops, knowing what was needed for sustainability.

Over the last half year, they'd achieved nothing short of a small miracle.

"The Army's latest triumph."

Thanks to the success on Ascension Island, the US Army was now in the process of establishing a formal hydroponics branch. New hydroponics farms would be built on the islands of Iwo Jima and Okinawa in the Pacific, in the Japanese city of Chofu on the western side of Tokyo, and even in far-flung locales like Iraq and Bahrain in the Persian Gulf. Within just a few years, the Army would be on track to grow more than 8 million pounds of fresh produce a year through hydroponics.

But perhaps most notably for the starstruck American public back home, RG and the guys had even gotten to rub shoulders with a real Hollywood celebrity. Kay Francis, the former number one star and highest paid actress at Warner Bros. movie studios, had arrived in a lavish entourage and spent an afternoon setting lettuce in the beds with the guys on the hy-droponics team, squatting right beside RG as she smiled and slid her hands into the earth.

"Kay Francis was not so wonderful – not that I ever thought so," RG later wrote Agnes, as if to reassure her he wasn't so enamored by celebrity.

Besides, he added, "They say she is 47!"

RG may not have thought much of the attention, but back home in Virginia, it was the talk of the town. Over the coming days, whenever Agnes left the house, people walked up to say they'd read about RG in the magazine. They stopped her at church, outside on the sidewalk, in the aisles of the grocery store. She would just smile and nod and say it was a swell write-up, thanking them for mentioning it.

It was a fine thing, the glow of local celebrity – a fine thing that lasted exactly one week, until it was outshined by the glow of an atomic bomb.

The movie star Kay Francis with the men of the hydroponics team as they plant lettuce into a new row of beds.

260 Evan Peter Smith

CHAPTER 68

⛧⛧

On August 15, the magazine covers on the rack at the
grocery store announced a complete and total victory
against Japan, after the United States had dropped two
atomic bombs over the Japanese cities of Hiroshima and Naga-
saki, killing hundreds of thousands of civilians in two radiant
blips.

Just about every magazine devoted its entire issue to the
news.

Inside that week's edition of "Life" magazine, alongside ads
for Chesterfield cigarettes, Firestone tires, Listerine shaving
cream and Live Savers candy, columnists debated the signifi-
cance of the moment.

"The people of the world, although thrilled by peace, were
shaken by the new weapon which had brought it about," one
columnist wrote.

A close-up photograph of the man who had directed the
atomic bombing of Japan, Gen. Carl "Tooey" Spaatz, was featured on that edition's cover: a grizzled hard-boiled man with
a lit cigarette stabbed between his teeth. Agnes saw the man's
face sitting on her family's coffee table after her father had finished reading through the copy that night.

"Wouldn't it be an odd thing," Spaatz told the magazine, "if
these were the only two atomic bombs ever dropped?"

When Agnes' father shut off the lamp to head to bed, darkness fell over Spaatz' face

CHAPTER 69

~~✤ ✤~~

By autumn, Agnes got a letter from RG with news that he would soon be heading back home. New guys were being flown to the island, he explained. They were being replaced.

He was finally put on a plane in early November and flown back to Brazil, and from Brazil hopped on a flight that took him to the United States.

But he wasn't sent home, not just yet.

Instead, the Air Force command had one last big task for one of the members of the famous hydroponics team.

He was flown to Wright-Patterson Air Force Base in Columbus, Ohio, where he was honored for his groundbreaking achievement in agricultural science by being put to work doing just about any menial task the Air Force could find.

Scrubbing toilets, mopping floors, laundry.

He'd become a janitor.

Talking to him on the phone, Agnes said it sounded to her "like a dirty deal" after all their success, and RG had just laughed into the receiver.

"Sure is," he said, "sure is."

Agnes couldn't be upset, though. For the first time this year, she'd finally gotten to hear her husband's voice. Now that RG was on base in Ohio, they'd been able to speak over the phone at least once every few days. Agnes would hold the phone up to their baby daughter's ear while RG sweet-talked through the receiver. She even got Agnes Gray to mutter a few giggles and gurgles for RG to hear her voice.

By the time Thanksgiving rolled around, RG said it would only be another few weeks until he'd be sent home.

We'll have Christmas to look forward to, he wrote her.

Agnes wrote back saying it'd better be the last holiday they'd ever spend apart.

A few days after Thanksgiving, she made another trip to the grocery store, walking down Liberty Street in the afternoon sunlight. The leaves in the trees had faded, the street a sepia-toned version of itself, pumpkins and squash on the stoops, and the shoppers who stepped through the entrance of the grocery store up ahead wore sweaters and long dresses. After following them inside, Agnes made her usual pass by the magazine rack once again, where all the latest editions of "The Saturday Evening Post," "Good Housekeeping," "Collier's," "Time," "Harper's," "National Geographic," and "Life" were spread out, their bright covers arranged to catch the eye of browsing shoppers.

Most of the magazine covers were still Thanksgiving-themed. The cover of "Good Housekeeping" showed a cute little girl with curled hair holding a fork and knife, bouncing in her chair as she waited for her Thanksgiving turkey, while "The Saturday Evening Post" featured a Norman Rockwell painting of a returned soldier in uniform and his mother peeling potatoes.

But the cover of that week's edition of "Life" magazine had nothing to do with the recent holiday – nothing to do with anything, as far as shoppers like Agnes could tell.

Instead, the cover showed a picture of a beautiful young blonde woman posing with one hand placed delicately on her thigh. The woman wore her hair tied up in a bun, her plump lips smeared with glossy red lipstick, while her impossibly tiny waist was synched tight by a large black belt.

The one and only headline on the cover read: "Big belts."

It was hardly worth stopping to take another look, especially for Agnes, who'd spent enough time over winter worrying about her own waistline without needing this model to make her feel bad too.

So she walked right past it.

She paid for her groceries at the counter and then exited the store, thinking nothing of that skinny blonde girl and her "big belt."

But how terribly strange, it would later seem, that the editors of "Life" had decided to put a fetching blonde gal on the cover of a magazine that spent the bulk of its pages explaining how the world was about to end.

And strangest of all, how Agnes' own husband had played a part in it.

CHAPTER 70

∗∗∗🎗 🎗∗∗∗

W henever he got to the edge of the city, RG was met with a flat ocean of razed farmland rolling in the distance, the golden waves of high corn having been buzzed away for harvest a few weeks before their arrival at Wright-Patterson Air Force Base. Now he saw wagons pass by in those barren fields, far away, like lone boats drifting on the ocean horizon.

Once again, he felt like he was on an island.

But life on Wright-Patterson in Columbus, Ohio, had its improvements. It was autumn, for one, and the air was cool, and the trees offered so many shades of color, the golden leaves dripping with rain some days, rustling musically in the breeze on others. Instead of bomber planes roaring across the sky over the ocean, he saw birds drifting in smooth flight patterns as they headed South toward warmer weather.

RG hoped he would be joining them soon enough.

For now, a few nights a week, he talked to Agnes on the phone. He told her he was confident he would see her before Christmas. The plan was for her to drive down to the farm in Watauga in early December, get settled at the brick house, and meet him at the bus station later that week in Boone.

Until then, he'd remain on base, scrubbing toilets, emptying trash cans, and mopping floors.

All the while, a part of him still wishing he were back on the island.

It was hard to put into words. And it wasn't the work here on base, either. Scrubbing toilets wasn't bad. RG had dealt with much worse back on the farm, although a base full of soldiers did give the hogs a run for their money, slop-wise.

But that wasn't it, no.

It was something else, something even he didn't quite understand.

When he'd been on the island, all he'd wanted was to be back in the states. Now that he was so close to home, he found himself walking down the halls of Wright-Patterson with his mop and bucket and his mind would wander back to the hydroponics station, how it felt to wander down the rows of vibrant tomato plants with the sunlight slanting through the mosquito netting. Touching the leaves with his fingertips, breathing in the smell of them. He still worried over how the plants were doing. Now, in this metropolis of more than 300 buildings intricately weaved together into one elaborate complex, with some 50,000 enlisted men flowing through its arteries, RG stood in the middle of it all and thought about roots and nutrient solution and propagation. It was a habit he hadn't yet unlearned. From January to October, a full ten months, it had been his entire life. Then they'd uprooted him and dropped him down here, in this labyrinth of cold steel and lifeless concrete, handed him a mop, and told him this was who he was now.

It was hard to believe he and rest of the hydroponics team had been on the cover of "National Geographic" a little more than three months earlier.

CHAPTER 71

H e missed the guys. RG hadn't gotten to see any of them once he'd left the island. He wasn't sure where they'd all ended up.

Earlier that summer, before the war in Japan had ended, while they were still on the island, all the guys had figured they'd be sent off to the Pacific Theatre for a massive invasion.

"For a lot of the fellows it looks like they will go on to the Pacific," he'd written Agnes in late June. "It would suit us fine to be left out."

Meanwhile, during those uncertain weeks on the island, they hadn't had much reassurance as to their fate. From the start of summer, Professor Blodgett had become a ghost, off on trips to Washington, D.C., and thence onward to British Ghana, just south of Trinidad, where a new hydroponics installation was supposedly being set up.

"There may be other people who will be sorry when the war is over but I am sure he is not one," RG had written about the professor. "He has been so afraid it would end and he would cease to be the great man he thinks he is."

Without the leadership of the Col., who'd gone off on other business himself, the guys on the island doubted whether the professor could coordinate his theories into practice, so they weren't surprised when word came back that more assistance was needed on the project in Africa. First, the higherups told Jones that he would be sent off to Ghana. Then they took Buckley, RG's tentmate. The guys in the tent all gave Buckley a grand farewell and told him to enjoy spending more time with "the old man."

A few other guys on the team heard rumors about possibly being sent to Roberts Field Airport in Liberia, where another hydroponics installation was starting up. Still others were sent to far luckier locales. "Some of the hydro boys went to Honolulu for a project there and are having a grand time," RG wrote. All the while, he waited for word of what would become of him.

In August, just a few days after the atomic bombs were dropped and Japan surrendered, a major by the name of Simpson arrived on the island with 16 new men who, RG was told, would serve as the replacements for the hydroponics team, although still he had his doubts.

"We have been told so many stories we don't believe them," he told Agnes. "The only thing I want is to get home to you."

By the end of September, a boat came through and took more than 400 guys off the island, but RG still had to wait nearly two more months before his exit ticket arrived.

So it was that he found himself as the last one in his tent, alone at night as he had been when he'd first arrived. The cots lay empty around him. No trunks on the floor, no sound. By his feet were his warm moccasins, the heels of which were all worn out now by all the months he'd spent in them. Every letter he'd written to Agnes, he'd been wearing these tasseled moccasins. Every night goofing around in the tent, talking with the guys, they'd been comfortably on his feet.

Now as he slipped on his moccasins and fiddled with the radio's antenna in the empty tent, he remembered a night from months earlier, just after the president had died, and a particularly strange moment that still stuck in his mind. It'd been one of those late nights, when the guys had all been listening to the final news broadcast of the day. News reports on the island came over the radio four times a day, first at 7:30 a.m., then just after lunch at 12:30, and right around dinner time at 5 p.m., with a summary of the day's events at 11 at night before the radio signal signed off.

That night, because it was still in the first week after President Roosevelt had died, the 11 o'clock summary played a broadcast of a transcript of the late president's speech at Yalta, followed by a remembrance in Roosevelt's honor, and then the signal signed off.

But no one had felt like sleeping, so one of the guys – RG couldn't remember now if it'd been Kurt, Buckley or Bill – had started messing around with the radio's antenna, and they'd all started joking about detecting alien signals up in the clouds.

But then it wasn't a joke, because they really *did* hear something.

A strange voice-like murmur began humming beneath the roiling surf of static. It made no sense: the radio broadcast on the island had been turned off. At first, they froze and just listened, confused. Voices surfaced from the static, then dove down again. With each small tap of the radio's antenna, other voices rose into clarity. They all heard it: different sounds, not random but distinct, like multiple conversations happening at once in the same room.

"We picked up a program of Latin music," RG later wrote. "Then we got a German program, so we thought, and then two or three other stations that were in Brazil or Africa. We just could not believe it."

The guys didn't know such a thing was possible. They moved the antenna like a divining rod, finding other voices, other sounds – the radio waves having traveled over the ocean like skipped stones, from Germany, France, Africa, Brazil. Voices from nations which were still at war with one another, talking all at once, in a small tent on an island in the middle of the ocean, while a group of guys who'd all grown up on farms without electricity sat in silence and listened.

Now, alone in the tent, RG switched off the radio and lay back on his cot, hearing only the wind.

CHAPTER 72

꧁ ꧂

As long as the wait was for news of his departure, when they finally told RG he was leaving the island, there wasn't much warning.

One morning in November they let him know that he'd be on the next plane, which would be flying out later that day. RG spent the next few hours packing up his things – his letters from Agnes, his souvenirs from the island, stuff he'd purchased at the PX, along with a pair of gator skin heels and matching gator skin purse for Agnes he'd got from a vendor back in Brazil and had been stowing under his cot ever since. He stopped by the post office and arranged to have his mail rerouted to Wright-Patterson. Then he said goodbye to some of the guys he knew who were still on the island and had one last meal in the chow hall.

But just before heading to Wideawake Field where the plane was waiting, RG couldn't help but make one last stop by the hydroponics site. He found the new team of guys were hard at work, pruning plants and monitoring the nutrient solution, carving out new growing beds for the site's expansion. They were a good group who'd learned well, but none of them, RG felt, had known the plants the way he and the original team had. From the new guys' perspective, this flourishing greenhouse spread over 80,000 square feet had been here from the start. They hadn't known the ashen wind wailing through the emptiness of this field back when there was nothing here, or the backbreaking work of carving out all the beds from scratch, or the doubt over whether such a task was even possible. They hadn't tucked each plant into the beds by hand as they'd done, and they certainly hadn't lost sleep over them. And how could they? None of them had even known this place had existed.

When his plane finally took off from Wideawake Field, RG looked out the window at the hydroponics site as they rose higher and higher. Obscured though it was by the cloth strips and mosquito netting, the exuberant green of the plant life within was still visible, still beautiful, the only bright sign of life over a barren wasteland. He could see blobs of shadows moving under the covering, which were the men going back and forth as they tended to the plants, like monks at the monastery, and he realized this is what all the folks in planes that'd been landing and taking off from Ascension must've seen over the last ten months, watching their progress from above, just as the birds had done.

How strange it looked, how wonderful.

Then the plane turned toward the ocean's horizon, toward home, and he never saw it again.

The land was barren when the hydroponics team arrived. Months later, it was transformed.

CHAPTER 73

ife at Wright-Patterson Air Force Base that autumn was dull by comparison, but there were small surprises.

One morning, RG was eating breakfast in the chow hall when a young man across the table made a gesture to get his attention.

"Aren't you from Boone?" the young man asked.

RG said yes, he was – well, born and raised in Valle Crucis, and now he ran a farm in Vilas, or he had done so before being drafted – but sure, Boone was close enough.

The boy said he'd thought so. He was from West Jefferson himself and had attended school in Boone while RG had been a teacher there at the high school. Vocational agriculture was his subject, correct?

RG nodded over his breakfast tray.

"He didn't take agriculture and I did not remember him," RG later wrote Agnes, but the young man seemed to remember RG well from those days. He'd even asked about that famous cross country road trip RG had coordinated during the summer of 1936, the "Southwestern Tour," as the newspapers had called it. His elaborate journey with all the kids in the back of a rattling Chevy truck, going from the Tennessee Valley to the Mississippi River, New Orleans and the Gulf of Mexico, and even crossing the border into Mexico – the young man still remembering the route by heart, evidently, which took RG by surprise even more than being recognized had.

It was a conversation that stuck with him the rest of the day.

His memories of that "Southwestern Tour" returned more vividly than they had in years. He remembered the weeks leading up to their departure. The conversations he'd had with the parents. The favors he'd asked. The money he'd raised for the kids who couldn't afford it. And then after they'd set off, the messy plans and mix-ups on their journey, like the time one of the boys got lost for more than a day on the Mexican border, or when their trailer broke off and all their supplies went tumbling down a ravine.

But all these years later, what he remembered most about the summer of 1936, during that time of poverty, hunger and despair, was all the kindness they'd found at each stop along the way.

The farmer who'd welcomed them onto their land and hosted a cookout.

The shrimper who'd taken them out onto the chopping waves and introduced them to the ocean.

The mother along the border who'd cooked them a full meal and treated each boy like he was her own.

And the world of opportunity that had unfurled before them, a promise of a future beyond anything those boy could imagine.

Now as RG pushed his mop down the halls of Wright-Patterson, he got to thinking of his old students again. Agnes had asked him what he planned to do when he got back to the farm, and it was true he'd briefly thought about the prospect of returning to teaching. Even though he still harbored that old dream of becoming a veterinarian, the idea of returning to the classroom had been pulling at him, a gentle but consistent tug. He just wasn't sure. "I have not decided yet what I want to do when I finally get back," he'd replied. "I think I will just wait and see what the score is on my return."

When he thought of his old students now, he couldn't get over how strange it was that those mountain boys who'd once sat in his classroom truly had, just a few years later, all been sent around the world – one old student sent off to the northern hills of France, another to the rain-bogged uplands of England, and still others in the factories of Detroit, the chopping waves of the Atlantic Theatre, and the snow-capped peaks of the Aleutian Islands.

And some, sent to their deaths.

It was so easy to remember a time when their stations in life had been purely symbolic, back when they'd all stood in formation at the start of their Future Farmers of America meetings, one of the after-school extracurriculars that were a part of the school's vocational agriculture program. The FFA meetings were a chance for the students to hone their skills, their values, their expertise and their leadership potential as young farmers. As their FFA advisor, RG would stand off in the corner of the room and simply observe as they ran through the official opening ceremony. At the start of each meeting, the students all donned matching blue jackets and observed the ceremony with an almost meditative formality. It was the closest thing to a ritual outside of the church that any of these farm boys had experienced – as natural as breathing to those who partook, but likely as strange as a rain dance to any outsider.

But so be it.

First, the student president of the FFA would rap on the podium to secure order, and the group's vice president would run a roll call of all the student officers, making sure to refer to them by their formal station titles.

"The sentinel?" the vice president would call out.

Speaking up like a soldier, the sentinel would reply, "Stationed by the door."

"Your duties there?" asked the vice president.

"Through this door pass many friends of the FFA," the sentinel would proclaim. "It is my duty to see that the door is open to our friends at all times and that they are welcome."

The ceremony would proceed, RG watching as the vice president called upon all officers and their symbolic stations.

"The reporter?"

"The reporter is stationed by the flag," the reporter would reply.

"The treasurer?"

"Stationed at the emblem of Washington," said the treasurer.

"The secretary?"

"Stationed by the ear of the corn," said the secretary.

"The advisor?"

"Here by the owl," said RG, stepping forward from his spot in the corner.

Back in those days, all those years ago, he'd only ever wanted one thing for his students. There were countless skills they needed to learn, of course, and techniques to master, theories to understand. But the one goal he'd been set upon during his years as a teacher had been simple:

He wanted his students to be proud.

For them to know that the worn soles of their boots and the tatters of their trousers were a sign of hard work, not poverty. That the early mornings and late nights on the farm were evidence of grit, not despair. And that the station of their birth, raised in a lineage of agriculture in the mountains of North Carolina, was as honorable as that of any president, movie star or general in the world.

To be a farmer was also to be an agronomist, mechanic, chemist, accountant, marketer, engineer, person of faith and more.

It was, he told them in the classroom, just about the most important job in the world.

That time and place was gone now, clear as ever in RG's mind, but as distant as they'd all drifted from the mountains of their birth. Scattered across the world – some wounded, some gone forever, some changed in ways unseen. And yet even now, having spoken the words of that FFA ceremony so many times, RG could mouth them without thinking as he pushed his mop down the dirty hallways of an Air Force base in Ohio.

"Here by the owl," he would say.

"Why by the owl?" asked the vice president.

"The owl is a time-honored emblem of knowledge and wis-dom," RG replied. "Being older than the rest of you, I am asked to advise you from time to time, as the need arises. I hope that my advice will always be based on true knowledge and ripened with wisdom."

But now, to him, that seemed like a joke, a punchline.

He'd only been 23 years old, barely out of college, when he'd first uttered those words – a kid himself. What "true knowledge" could he have known? What experience "ripened with wisdom" could he have possibly imparted? And after all these years of war, what could he say now to a group of young men who'd spent the prime of their lives fighting through carnage and bloodshed all over the world, while he'd been on some island in the middle of the ocean, gardening tomatoes and lettuce?

Not to say he wasn't proud of the work the hydroponics team had done. They'd gone against daunting odds and had gotten the job done – true to their stations as farmers. But he also knew it would never be the stuff of a Hollywood movie. They weren't flying airplanes or defeating Nazis. They weren't torpe-doing U-boats to the bottom of the ocean. They were just try-ing to grow some fresh food for the guys doing the real work around them. It wasn't altogether different from RG's college years, back when he'd spent his days milking cows to ensure fresh dairy for the cadets. He and the rest of the hydroponics team had been like the men slopping food on trays in the chow hall, or the guys manning the booth at the post office, or the countless janitors – as RG was now – who kept the bases decent and functioning, playing a minor part on a grand stage. It was something to hang your hat on, but it wasn't anything the gen-erals would applaud or even notice.

Which is why it was all the more unbelievable when, later that week, a major feature story appeared in the Nov. 19, 1945, edi-tion of "Life" magazine.

A story in which a four-star general not only noticed RG and the hydroponics team but took great pains to tell the Secretary of War, the Joint Chiefs, and the entire nation about them, while warning of a nightmare ahead that could cast the world into eternal darkness.

And a group of young men, quiet as owls, who'd been living in that darkness all along, without even knowing.

CHAPTER 74

N othing about the cover of that edition of "Life" magazine
gave any indication of the horrors contained within its
pages.

"Big belts," read the headline on the cover of the Nov. 19 issue,
along with a picture of a blonde cover model posing in a stylish
outfit.

Nothing about the few dozen pages that followed gave any
indication either that this edition of the magazine would be
particularly noteworthy. Ads for B.F. Goodrich tires promised
"better synthetic rubber – different from the ordinary synthetic
rubber in general use by the tire industry." Forhan's toothpaste
claimed that four out of five Americans may already have Gin-
givitis, warning that even slightly bleedings gums were a sure
sign of a diseased mouth. General Electric offered a brand-new
radio with "natural color tone" audio capabilities, while movie
star and phenom dancer Betty Hutton claimed that Bexel Vita-
min B complex capsule "pep pills" were her secret to success,
promising "popularity, gaiety, romance" to become "a blonde
bundle of T.N.T." like she was on the big screen.

RG and the rest of the guys had to flip through all those advertisements and more, pages and pages of them, just to get to
the major feature story in that week's edition. Finally, on page
27, beside an unintentionally ironic ad for the Prudential Life
Insurance Company, the story announced itself with a photo
illustration of Washington, D.C. being vaporized in a nuclear

explosion, along with the headline, "The 36-Hour War: Arnold Report Hints At the Catastrophe Of The Next Great Conflict."

What followed were 11 pages explaining the very likely end of the world, or at least the end of civilization, in the coming decade. It made the Prudential Life Insurance ad seem comical, because as far as the guys knew, insurance policies weren't all that reliable in a nuclear apocalypse.

The feature story was arguably the most alarming article ever printed in "Life" magazine's history up to that point, a detailed outline of the coming nuclear war. What terrified everyone who read it the most was the source of the information. This was not some science fiction fantasy or the work of Orson Welles but was, in fact, a beat-by-beat summary of the recently released, "Third Report of the Commanding General of the Army Air Force to the Secretary of War," written by the commander of the Air Force himself, Gen. H.H. Arnold.

The very same man, RG remembered, who had once toured the ashen fields of Ascension Island.

Addressing a celebratory nation, Arnold cautioned humility in the face of victory. "At times the margin of winning was narrow... many times we were near losing," he wrote in his report. "Our enemies' mistakes often pulled us through. In the flush of victory, some like to forget these unpalatable truths."

Now came the battles ahead.

"The start of another war, said General Arnold, might come with shattering speed," the article warned.

The general's nightmares were illustrated in detail over the pages that followed. Volleys of nuclear bombs rising and falling in elegant arcs from one side of the world to another. Futuristic outer space airplanes bearing precision rockets, orbiting above. Underground nuclear facilities operating like termite infestations. Men in radiation suits rummaging through the debris of Chicago. Dead women slumped in telephone operating rooms amid glass, coiled wire and debris. Widespread destruction, little hope for salvation.

"The danger zone of modern warfare is not restricted to the battle lines and adjacent areas but extends to the innermost parts of the nation," Arnold wrote.

His final assessment was bleak: "No one is immune from the ravages of war."

He told the nation that it needed to prepare itself for a world in which the atomic threat would be the driving force dictating global events for the remainder of the century, if not the remainder of time itself.

To do so, General Arnold listed the most critical new concepts that would have to be fully understood and developed to enable survival through the now-terminal nuclear age.

Those concepts were:

1. The influence of atomic energy on air power.
2. Jet propulsion / rockets.
3. Radar advancement.

But he warned there was still no good defense against an incoming attack. Even if the US developed a radar beam of enormous power to sweep the sky so objects thousands of miles in space would send back radio echoes, it would only give the nation about 30 minutes to get ready for an attack.

"But even 30 minutes is too little time," the general wrote.

He knew the score. "We should attempt to make sure that nowhere in the world are atomic bombs being made clandestinely," he said, but he was aware it was only a matter of time before the ability of an enemy nation to launch an atomic attack on the United States was not only possible but guaranteed. When that occurred, Arnold estimated that 40 million people would die in the short-term, and any city of more than 50,000 in population would be leveled. "San Francisco's Market Street, Chicago's Michigan Boulevard and New York's Fifth Avenue are merely lanes through the debris," the article in "Life" noted (the title of the magazine itself now seeming darkly ironic), while the vestiges of the American population lingered on the outskirts.

And yet, there was one ray of hope.

"In spite of the apocalyptic destruction caused by its atomic bombs, an enemy nation would have to invade the US to win the war," Arnold argued.

So the nation would need to be ready for that scenario, a world in which the United States hunkered down and prepared amidst the ruined and barren wasteland, scattered across the ravaged outskirts or hidden underground. To do so, Arnold had listed a fourth and final critical new concept, one that was just as important, he said, as the nation's air power and atomic energy and radar sweeps across the stars.

A concept the Air Force had already tested in a place most resembling that apocalyptic future of barren soil, harsh terrain and burned lifelessness.

A concept known as:

4. Hydroponics

"Ascension Island was picked as the first testing laboratory for large scale cultivation of vegetables by hydroponics," Arnold wrote in his report. "A party consisting of an officer, nine enlisted men, and a civilian expert landed on the 'rock' in January. A plot of land was taken over and engineers began construction of concrete beds which were filled with sifted volcanic gravel. Seedlings were planted; a nutrient solution, containing the chemicals necessary for the growth of plants, was passed through the beds from two reservoir tanks. Four months later these 'visiting farmers' were harvesting tomatoes, radishes, lettuce and cucumbers from an 80,000 square foot area of facility."

The success of those "visiting farmers" was so overwhelming that it would be repeated over and over, and god willing, all future American soldiers and civilians could also be able to repeat the process to survive in the ruins – if and when it came to that bleak outcome.

"Today hydroponics is an accepted fact and will have its place in the postwar AAF along with other products of science and research," Arnold continued. "Chemical gardens will be established at all remote installations where fresh vegetables cannot be grown by ordinary methods."

He ended his report on the hydroponics team with the following words:

"Important in itself, this development brings down to earth the need for a close partnership with science, and for the courage and foresight to translate experiment into practice."

For RG and the rest of the guys, making the cover of "National Geographic" had been one thing. Being singled out directly by a founding father of the US Air Force, on the other hand?

Well, that was something else entirely.

As far as anyone could tell, it was first and only time in American history that a four-star general had used the word "courage" to describe a group of guys growing tomatoes.

CHAPTER 75

I n December of 1945, another early snowfall coated the Southeast of the United States.

Driving down south early that month, Agnes often found herself as one of the few cars on the roadway.

Snow fell as she drove. She breathed quiet clouds of steam against the windshield. Other than the precious passenger asleep beside her, Agnes made the drive alone, more than 250 miles from Harrisonburg, VA, down to Watauga County, NC.

It was early in the day, and she took her time, going slowly down the roads through the continuing but light snowfall. She wore her winter coat and gloves, as the temperature was well below freezing, while Agnes Gray wore a woolen cap on her still-mostly bald head. Every few moments, Agnes turned to glance at her daughter, keeping her right hand up to ensure Agnes Gray remained steady during even the smallest of turns. The baby was seated in a comfortable setup in the passenger seat, her feet cozy in her fuzzy one-piece jumper. For once, she was not crying. The lullaby of wheels turning beneath her and the vision of swirling snow out the window had put her in a trance, and now she was deep asleep, milk drunk and drooling, and heading home for the first time.

It was a few hours before Agnes reached the spread of mountains that served as the entrance to Watauga County.

But when she did, she saw the snow-covered peaks and drove onward into a bright and temporary world where everything glimmered and gleamed, as if undiscovered, passing through tunnels with icy branches bending over and dripping like fresh rain in the glow. Shrubbery along the road had frozen as if in shock. Squirrels leaped overhead like dancers, the branches bending and shedding snow. Sunlight dazzled everything. She felt herself finessing the wheel and navigating through this beautiful danger, around tight curves and up steep slopes, down slippery spots of gravel and along cliffsides, just as RG had done on those cool spring nights when she'd first visited the farm with him all those years ago.

Only this time, staring straight ahead with the wheel in her gloved hands and her baby beside her, Agnes didn't flinch.

CHAPTER 76

꙳

The house had missed her.

Dust coated stairwell bannisters, coated furniture, shelves, and books, coated every spot on the floor that hadn't been disturbed by the footsteps of its lone occupant – RG's father Ed, who regarded Agnes with a silent nod as he proceeded to gradually vacate his presence from the house the moment she and her daughter arrived.

Ed had spent the war living here in this house that had once belonged to his brother and now belonged to his son. Though still technically married, Ed was a bachelor now, more of a hermit. He lived among cattle and the farm workers who lived on the land and was perfectly content with weeks, even months, of near total silence. Agnes wouldn't have been surprised if the man had used the same spoon, bowl, fork, knife and plate over the years he'd been holed up here. It was doubtful that all but one of the chairs at the kitchen table had been moved by his hand since Agnes had left this house years ago. A housekeeper had attended to the house during that time, but with the harsh weather the upkeep had been neglected over the last few weeks.

Ed still occupied one of the bedrooms in the house until RG arrived here, but he was out from sunrise until sunset working the fields and tending to the livestock in the snow, warming himself in the barn by smoking cigar after cigar, and he drafted through the house like a ghost when home, lavishing the air with the fragrances of burley tobacco and earthy muck as he quickly barricaded himself in his room. He rarely spoke, and this was fine by Agnes. She had enough work on her hands bringing the house back in shape and caring for the baby. Silence was something she savored. The wind outside howled loud enough.

On her first night at the house, a light snowfall had fluttered outside in the fields, and snow had kept falling ever since. "Tuesday night was fierce and we had no electricity from 5:30 Tues until about 12:30 Wed," she wrote RG. "Last night was terrible I nearly froze. So hurry home. I miss you so much."

Agnes felt like a pioneer, holed up for the winter.

"The cold weather continues in this area, with mercury Tuesday and Wednesday morning standing at slightly below ten degrees," noted the latest edition of the *Watauga Democrat,* "but this morning there are evidences of clearing skies, and hopes are that the cold wave which began a week ago, may be definitely broken soon. Much of the snow which fell the first of last week yet remains."

Meanwhile, life went on.

Down the road at the Boone demonstration school, the elementary school children were preparing for their program of Christmas music planned for Sunday, Dec. 16, at 2:45 in the Boone Baptist Church. "Parents and friends of the school are cordially invited to come and hear the children render the story of Christmas in carols," read the invitation. With the continuing snowfall, travel was difficult, but the invitation added, "It is hoped that the parents and friends of the children will make a special effort to come." While the snow piled up in the valley and the mountains, one Mrs. W. M. Burwell, speaking on behalf of the Boone Bird Club, expressed hope that "the people of the community and county will think of the birds during the snowy weather, when food is unavailable, and place bread scraps and other food where the song birds may eat it," the *Watauga Democrat* reported. "Mrs. Burwell also respectfully requests that the boys refrain from shooting or otherwise destroying the birds."

Agnes had little time to read the paper. She was too busy dusting off the cobwebs of a home that had sat idle for too long – brightening up rooms, cleaning grime, doing all she could to banish a lingering odor of decay that had been marinading the air for years. She smacked rugs as if she were relieving anger. She fought with the scum and muck that had accumulated in sinks and toilets, and she spent hours polishing the dining room table. "I have worked up a storm with heaps still to be done," she wrote RG. "And Agnes Gray doesn't appreciate – had to pull her pen out in the dining room so she could watch. She looked at me so funny."

When she wasn't scrubbing floorboards or wiping down countertops, she was looking after Agnes Gray, who seemed to be adjusting poorly at first to the new environment. "Our 'Wee One' hasn't been feeling so good the last couple of days, has had diarrhea and for the life of me I can't figure out any reason for her pest," Agnes told RG. "Thought she was better yesterday afternoon but she took a turn for the worse last night and neither of us slept very much. Changed diaper all night. Gave her some medicine, crackers and water and she is feeling much better this afternoon – and I sure hope she sleeps tonight... The poor little Dolly has circles under her eyes... Tell the officials to hurry and give you that discharge so you can get home posthaste, your wife and daughter are powerful lonesome for you."

The next day, a letter from RG arrived that said his discharge was still uncertain. He hoped he'd be back by Christmas, but so far, he'd had no word that it would happen.

Agnes wasn't pleased. "To say that the news in your letter yesterday morn was disappointing is putting it very mildly," she wrote back. "...But that's the Army!"

She'd finally gotten the house in decent shape, and they had money now too. That day, she'd gone off to the tobacco market with RG's father for the latest sale. They'd done well, had brought in $1,129. And Agnes had managed to get the house "warm as toast," she said, ever since she'd stubbornly convinced the wood stove, coal fireplace and oil heater to behave themselves.

"Another Sunday is almost over, and I am getting more and more impatient for you to be home and spending Sunday and all the other days with your family," she told RG. "Yesterday was very cold, damp and dreary. I am so anxious to know each and every day's events and especially with regard to your coming home. I miss you so horribly, it has been such a long, long time since you left me."

"It will be heavenly to be tight in your arms again," she added.

As Christmas approached and RG's discharge was still just out of reach, as Agnes balanced her time between attending to the needs of Agnes Gray and working to get the house in shape, she took a moment to step back and look at the little girl her daughter had become. Agnes Gray was still a tiny thing, but there was a good healthy color and shape to her face, and now that she'd gotten over her weariness at the harsh cold on the farm, she'd gained a resilient glow in her eyes. Even compared to other little girls, she was constantly curious. Her big eyes seemed intent upon absorbing the world entire, while she gripped at everything before her, bouncing and eager for anything new. "She looks all around and her little hands fly," was how Agnes described her in a letter to RG.

One thing she still hadn't mentioned to her husband, one thing she was going to keep for herself, was an image that she would hold in her mind for the rest of her life. There was no way to remove it from her memory, and for this reason alone, she had decided never to force it upon RG – the image that arose especially late at night, when her nerves were at their worst:

The shriveled, diseased, almost lifeless creature that Agnes had seen when she'd been wheeled into the preemie room of the hospital to look at their daughter for the first time.

Over the weeks and months that had followed that moment, whenever RG had asked for a photo of their little daughter, she'd begged off. Sometimes, Agnes had just plain ignored the request. Other times, she'd come up with any reason why she wasn't able to get a photo sent his way just yet. She'd been stalling, waiting. And when he'd asked for her to at least send another photo of herself, she'd done the same thing, knowing that the dark bags under her eyes, the skeleton pallor of her face, and the wrinkled stress lines was not something she wanted him to see.

So she'd waited. For weeks. For months. Until spring had arrived, when the sunlight had ignited the dust motes in her family's living room like flecks of gold, and Agnes had posed in a fine new dress with her smiling baby girl in her arms, Agnes Gray sucking on a tiny bottle. Her sisters had snapped the camera over and over, and later Agnes had chosen the best few to send to him.

RG wrote back saying, "The pictures were so sweet... the one with the bottle was so especially sweet. She sure looks like a little Darling."

He'd added, "I sure wish we could have gotten a few shots when she was so very very small and still in the hospital."

But Agnes knew she had made the right decision.

The past was the past. She only wanted to move forward with her life.

Now, at the brick house, she'd been busy all the last week polishing the banisters of the stairwell, scrubbing the floors, dusting the ceiling and wiping down the countertops, as if trying to convince him – and herself too – that nothing had changed.

But of course, everything had changed.

CHAPTER 77

J ust a few days before Christmas, 1945, as snow was falling all through the mountains, a Salvation Army Santa Clause stood by the entrance of the bus station in downtown Boone, ringing his bell for donations. Dressed in his fluffy outfit, he called out thanks as people dropped coins in his kettle.

Cold air whipped through the bus station's doors whenever someone walked in or out.

Agnes felt the chill waft on her bare arms, even though she was standing across the room. Another late snowfall had blown in that night, so she was standing by the window inside the station, looking out as she waited for the bus to arrive. She'd already been waiting so long, her arms were burning from holding Agnes Gray, while snow swirled in the lamppost light on the street. She would've sat down, but she was too nervous.

She wasn't even sure what she was waiting for. RG had said tonight might be the night in a letter that had made its way to the farmhouse that morning, saying that he'd been discharged and that he'd be setting off by bus from Ohio to North Carolina in a few days. He sent it early, so she would have time to prepare, but another weather delay meant the letter had taken days to get here, so she'd had to rush that morning to prepare for his arrival – or at least, the promise of his arrival.

It was especially uncomfortable to wait alone. She knew everyone at the bus station could tell why she was here. They'd all seen her type before these last few months: a young women dressed up far too pretty for any regular old trip to the bus station. And that nervous look on her face and the way she was constantly glancing out the window – and the little baby in her arms too – only made it more obvious. Scenes like this one had been enacted countless times as more boys came back from overseas. She probably would've seen that Salvation Army Santa Clause glancing her way too, had she not been too shy to look.

It occurred to her, as she stood looking out at the falling snow, that exactly five years to the day had passed since she and RG had met for the first time inside that church in Independence, Virginia, in December of 1940, back when she was just some girl playing the piano, and he was the polite stranger in coat and tie, newly arrived in town.

All these years, and yet it felt as if she were meeting him for the first time all over again.

She looked out at the street suddenly aglow, the falling snow illuminated, as a bus pulled into the station.

The breath left her body.

She felt immediately and horribly strange about how she looked, as if the headlamps of the bus had illuminated all of her flaws. How exactly is a woman supposed to dress when meeting her husband again after more than a year apart? And she wasn't sure what she would say to him. Their first few years as a couple had been mostly long distance anyway, conducted through letters and phone calls, and they'd only been married a short time before he was shipped away. It was hardly incorrect to say they'd spent more time apart than they had together. And it hadn't been an easy past year, either. So many nights without sleep, so many days sick in bed. Had she changed too much?

Had he?

Through the window, she watched the bus lurch to a stop, the *shhhh* of the brakes sighing in the cold winter air, steam clouds rising from beneath its belly of pipes and vents. The door swung open just as Agnes was stepping outside herself with the baby. The cold was harsh on her, but she didn't even feel it. She'd already had goose bumps all the last hour.

Standing on the curb, she waited as a stream of passengers disembarked from the bus, men and women, strangers, faceless people who might as well have been see-through.

And then, there he was.

Snow flurries cascaded in the space between them down the curb. From where she stood, he looked the same as she remembered, only tanner, a bit leaner, his shoulders even broader now from the work on the island. He glowed in the lamppost light. It was a shock how dashing he looked in his uniform.

If anyone else was watching her now, Agnes didn't notice.

She waited, the baby in her arms, until his eyes fell on her.

Then she smiled, without even realizing it.

He stepped forward. She watched him move through the light. Apparently, RG didn't even care about his bags because he let them drop on the ground as he moved toward her, and the moment he reached out to her, the world paused. The snow seemed to stop falling. The people stood still on the sidewalk. The wind fell silent. There was only his body and hers, all the memories of his touch rushing back to her again.

They kissed in the flurries under the lamppost light while the snow cascaded over the mountains behind them.

Only when RG stepped back, getting a good look at her, did the rest of the world start moving again.

Agnes didn't know what to say. Standing in the falling snow, her cheeks red and streaked with tears, she managed to whisper, "Agnes Gray, meet your Daddy," and she handed the baby over to him.

In the coming days and weeks, Agnes knew she would have to learn to live with this man again. His weight and warmth in the bed beside her. His toothbrush in the bathroom. His muddy boots by the door. There would be a cold winter ahead of them. The farm would need to be fixed up and the working schedule restructured under their guidance after so many years away. They would need to find work for themselves too, would need to decide how they would live for the next month, the next year, the next decade. They would care for their baby, and perhaps more babies would come. All the while, they would have to get used to the small things about each other, some remembered, some forgotten, and some not yet learned at all.

They would build a life together, in other words.

Whatever that looked like.

But even now, before all that, Agnes knew in her heart that she would remember this moment for the rest of her life: RG smiling as he took the baby and held her against his chest, and the little girl gazing up at him, her big eyes taking in the features of the unfamiliar man now holding her.

Agnes Gray looked so healthy, so happy. None of the people strolling around them in the bus station could have possibly known the pain this little girl had gone through – the pain Agnes herself had gone through on those dark winter nights, in quiet, alone. No one would've thought anything other than how sweet and simple a moment this was.

And for now, for her, that was enough.

"Well," RG said as the baby curled against him, "it certainly is nice to finally meet you, Agnes Gray."

With his bag over his shoulder, he carried their daughter, and Agnes walked alongside him back through the bus station. They stepped outside into the parking lot, passing by Santa Clause, who rang his bell and wished them all a Merry Christmas. Then they got in the car together, as a family, and drove down the snow-covered roads toward home.

THE END

AFTERWARD

By 1952, the US Army's special hydroponics branch grew more than 8 million pounds of fresh produce a year. Commercial hydroponics farms began to appear all over the United States in the decades that followed, especially in Florida. Hydroponics has been utilized in locales as diverse as Africa and Antarctica, South America and the Middle East, Asia and Europe, and even in outer space: NASA has experimented with hydroponically grown produce in the International Space Station through its controlled ecological life-support systems. The global hydroponics market size was estimated at $2.6 billion as of 2021.

ACKNOWLEDGEMENTS

I would like to thank the entire Shipley family, first and foremost, especially Janie, Agnes Gray, and Bobby (the children of RG and Agnes), who were integral to the creation of this book.

Deepest gratitude also to those whose research, input, and support brought this story to life, namely: my grandmother Janie Smith, aka "Granna," who spurred me to write this book in the first place; Hermann Trojanowski, whose oral history interview with RG served as the scaffolding to much of this narrative; Ashley Warlick and Lindsey DeLoach Jones, whose Writeshare program out of M Judson Books in Greenville, SC, brought this book from a sloppy mess to a significantly less sloppy mess; Heather Morris and Peter Kent, who offered early and instrumental feedback; and Rowe and John Carenen, who provided late-stage insight to polish up some rough patches.

Thank you to the National Archives for the use of historical photographs of Ascension Island.

I also want to thank my parents, Greg and Karen, my brother, PJ, and my sister, Courtney, for their lifelong support.

And most of all, endless thanks to my wife Haleigh, whose love and encouragement I can never repay. If I were RG, you would be my Agnes. Love you always.

CPSIA information can be obtained
at www.ICGtesting.com
Printed in the USA
BVHW051323221022
649854BV00002B/19

9 780578 310787